扉詩 1
Opening Poems 1

スコット・ワトスン
「20 山頭火」より
日本語原詩付

Scott Watson
From 20 Santoka:
with their original Japanese

松はみな枝垂れて南無観世音

Pine branches all bowing so be it Buddha

空へ若竹のなやみなし

Into sky young bamboo untroubled

鴉啼いてわたしも一人

Crow song I too am alone

茶の木にかこまれそこはかとないくらし

Surrounded by tea bushes nebulous living

曼珠沙華咲いてここがわたしの寝るところ

Higanbana blooming this is where I sleep

扉詩 2
Opening Poems 2

連句：恵道と野里子
Linked Haiku: Edo & Noriko

古橋や愛される季語投げようか（恵道）

an old bridge…

shall I throw off

beloved season words? (Edo)

古橋や火の風船に焦がされて（野里子）

an old bridge

balloon on fire may

burn it down (Noriko)

=========

消えて行く渋谷の夕日旧きビル（恵道）

Shibuya sunset

another building

bites the dust (Edo)

ハチ公のマスク新(あたら)し渋谷駅（野里子）

Shibuya station

Hachiko: his mask new

Corona times (Noriko)

パンドラ
目次

Pandora
Contents

杏平太（日本・千葉）

狐の嫁入り

まんまん　まんまん　まんまるい　潮満つ月の宵
きつねは　よめいり　いたします
かしこく　とがった　ふたつの　おみみ
みごとに　かくした　つのかくし
ほっぺの　ずるそな　おひげさえ
月影　映したように　みせまする
まんまん　まんまる　お月さま
どうか　わたしの願い　かなえてよ
ほんとは　やさしい　わたしの心
村のはずれの　お地蔵さまの
大きな胸の　あなたに　抱かれる
あぶらげ色の　みごとな
いねのほ　さらさら

あんがい　ぶっとい　わたしの　あんよ
目をつぶる　わたしは
あなたの　心のままに
たった　ひと夜の　こととても
まんまん　まんまる　お月さま
にこにこ　笑って　許してくれる
あなたは　わたしの　だいじな　だいじな　お婿さま

Peter Aprikott (Japan/ Chiba)

Wedding Procession for a Fox

Round and round, lovely round, full tidc and full moon.
a fox is leading a wedding procession.
Two bridal ears both pointed and wise,
hidden deftly inside the bridal hood.
Even the whiskers on the wily guests' cheeks,
seem to reflect the moonlight's shadows.
Round and round, lovely round, fulll tide and full moon.
oh please hear my wish and grant it for me.
Listen to the kindness I hide in my breast,
oh Mr. Jizo* sitting on the edge of the village.
Hold me against your breast so broad,
the great heads of rice, they rustle together,
the golden colour of a fried beancurd cake.
My legs may be fleshier than you expect,
but 1will close my eyes up tight,
And you can make free of me for just tonight,
our one and only nuptial night.
Round and round lovely round, full tide and full moon.
please smile on me and forgive this one night,
my dearest darling, dearest husband.

* A '*jizo*' is a guardian deity of chi1dren, and small statues of them can often be seen along roadsides, or dotted amongst urban dwellings.

崔龍源（日本・東京）

空のひとみ

わたしは捨てられた巫女
だからわたしの手は青白い
わたしは一度も結婚しなかった女
わたしの静脈は世界中をめぐる川になった
それはむかしむかしのこと
戦争が　歴史にしるされた無数の戦争が
わたしを　犯しつづけた　ゆえにわたしが
産んだ子どもたちもまた　戦争で
都市や町や村や草原を凌辱した
わたしの肩を踏みにじった軍靴
わたしの髪を燃やした焼夷弾
わたしの心臓を爛れさせた枯れ葉剤
わたしを一瞬に消し去った原爆
わたしを書いた書物はみな
戦火に焼けた　わたしはだから
存在していないのだ　どこにも
ただわたしのうわさだけが
民衆の口の端（は）にのぼり　わたしは彫像であったり
土器にきざまれた絵だったりした
わたしの乳房から　小麦は芽生えた
わたしの秘所から稲は生えた
わたしの唇から葡萄酒はあふれ
わたしは果樹園そのものでもあった
高層ビルの窓という窓から見える
風景の一部ではなく全体であった

Ryugen Sai (Japan/ Tokyo)

Eye in the Sky

I am a shrine maiden forsaken,
So my hands look pale.
I am a woman who never have got married,
My veins turned to a river circulating through the world.
It happened long ago.
Wars, numberless wars, which were recorded down in our history,
They continued to rape me. So my children I gave births to,
Violated cities, towns, villages, and grass fields,
Also in wars, they destroyed.
Military boots trampled on my shoulders,
Incendiaries scorched my hair,
Defoliants festered my heart,
Atomic bombs vapored me in an instant.
All the books that recorded me, were all burned by war fires,
So nowhere I exist in the world, except for my rumors,
Which were very often referred to by people's chats.
Sometime I was supposed to be a statue,
Sometime my figure was inscribed in earthenware pots.
Out of my breasts sprouted up wheat,
Out of my secret place grew up rice plants,
Between my lips did wine overflow,
I was an orchard, myself.
I was a whole view of the landscape you could see through,
From every window of skyscrapers: not a part.
But I was a vanishing point.

だが消失点でもあった
わたしが消えた地点から
地上のはじめの母は生まれたのだ
毛むくじゃらの　やっと二本足で立った彼女は
家族のしあわせを祈って死んだ
わたしは満足だった　彼女はつつましく
こころやさしかったから　わたしは彼女を誇りとした
アフリカの大地の緑
わたしはやがて一本の樹木となった
わたしの樹冠をかすめて飛ぶ鳥は
わたしをたたえて鳴いた
わたしの根元で眠るけものたちは
わたしにたくさんの喜びを与えてくれた
だがわたしは息子たちを失くした女
ホロコーストや難民キャンプで
息子を捜しつづける女
一度も結婚しなかったわたしにとって
世々生まれた息子たちはわたしの息子
世々地球議をまわしつづける子供たちも
ストリート・チルドレンも　地雷で
足を失くした少年兵も　戦車に
轢かれた老人も　ホームレスの男も
わたしがいちまいの枯葉でないとしたら
わたしは大地であるだろう
わたしが貝殻でないとしたら
わたしは海であるだろう
わたしはまだ名付けられていない
わたしはたしかに生まれたのだ
大地にはわたしの足跡があり
海辺にはわたしの築いた砂の城がある

From the spot where I vanished,
The first mother on the earth was born.
She was hairy and struggled to stand up with her two legs,
She died, praying for happiness of her family.
I was satisfied with her. She was modest.
She was tender. I was proud of her.
Green is the mother earth in Africa,
There I grew up into a tree.
Birds were flying, skimming just over my crown,
They sang songs in my praise,
Animals were sleeping at my roots,
They gave me so much rejoice.
But I am really a woman who lost my sons,
By the holocausts, or in refugee camps.
I am a woman who shall not stop looking for my sons.
I had never got married, So, to me,
The ones who have been born in this world are all my sons:
The boys who play turning globe miniatures,
Street children, young soldiers who lost their legs by mines,
An old man who was run over by the tank, and homeless men: all.
If I am not a dry leaf,
I shall be the earth.
If I am not a seashell,
I shall be the sea.
I am not given a name yet,
I was born to this world for sure.
The earth has my footprints,
The sea coast has my sand castle I constructed.
I am a life, forever.
If I am not a bird,

わたしは生きつづけている
わたしが一羽の鳥でないとしたら
わたしは広がる空であるだろう
ほら　空には　わたしを映しているひとみがある

I shall be a sky, spreading endless.
Look! There, you can see the eye reflecting me.

(Translator: Noriko Mizusaki)

林宏匡（日本・東京）
Hiromasa Hayashi (Japan/ Tokyo)

『ホルムスクの夕日』より
From *The Setting Sun in Holmsk* *

燃ゆるわが街：望郷の賦
My Town Burning : Nostalgia in My Boyhood

少年に軍靴は重し炎焔と燃ゆるわが街見かへりにつつ

The military shoes heavy for a boy: I walked,

Back looking at my town in flames burned.

砲声の絶えざる夜をはらからの名を呼び合ひてひた歩きけり

I walked on with hearing booming of guns,

Loud called brethren each to each the names.

わが街の夜空赫々染まりつつ離（さか）りゆけども砲声絶えず

The sky above my town got dyed in red,

Farther I was away the guns did not end.

離りゆく街の炎（ほむら）の赤き夜の樺の樹影はうつつに怪し

The town I parted from in flames red

At night, a birch the-shadow looked weird.

(Translator: Noriko Mizusaki)

＊訳者註：サハリン（樺太）の街のロシア名。日本語名は真岡。

＊Translator’s Note: It is a Russian name of a town in Sakhalin. The Japanese call it Maoka in Karafuto, where once they lived..

福

きしもとタロー（日本・京都）
Taro Kishimoto (Japan/ Kyoto)

言葉に敏感になるということ

2020年は、多くの人々にとって記憶に刻まれる年となった。新型コロナウィルス騒ぎで、世界が止まってしまったかのように感じられた人もいるかも知れないが、実はそんなことはない。

経済の動きは、止まっただろうか。いや、そんなことはない。今まで回っていたところで、回っていた量が回らなくなっただけで、その代わりにそれらはどこかに吸い上げられるようにして、別のところで動いている。ヒトの動きは止まっただろうか。いや、そんなことはない。実際、僕が暮らす田舎では、田植えや畑、草刈りや山の整備と、春以降はやることが山積みで、皆忙しそうにしていた。都市生活という、人類の歴史の中でも特異な状況・生活スタイルに関しては、多少停滞気味だったかも知れないが、自然に近いところで暮らしている人々にとっては、そうでもない。要は、自然は人間の都合で立ち止まってはくれないということだが、だとすると人間の状況で止まってしまったかのように見えている世界とは、一体どういう世界なんだろう。

また、この機会に生き方を見直し、新しいことを始めた人々もいた。クライシス（crisis）という言葉が「危機」という意味であることは知っていても、その一方で「転換」という意味があることを知る人は少ない。たとえば、家にいる時間が増えたことで、生き方そのものを見直し、家族の在り方・仕事のやり方を問い直すきっかけにした人々もいた。学校に行かなくてもよくなった田舎の子供たちの中には、毎日外で遊び、好きな本を読み、田んぼの手伝いをし、年齢の離れた大人とたちと会話し、そして遊び、気が付けば一ヶ月そこらで、それまで自分から大人に話しかけたりはしなかったのに、自分から積極的に話しかけるようになった子供もいた。

テレビが「見せている」ものだけが、情報の全てではないし、それだけが重要な情報という訳でもない。より良い変化を遂げているものを見せられなければ、悪いことしか起きていないようにも思えるだろう。止まっていると言われれば、止まっているようにも思えるだろうし、危ないと言われれば、危ないものにしか見えてこないかも知れない。しかし、確かめようのない情報を言葉通りに受け取り、それを唯一の事実であるかのように思い込むのは、あまりに危険だ。

僕は音楽家なので、いつも世の中を行き交う言葉の響きに引っかかってしまう。言葉という音が、その人の中で何を表しているのか、人々の間で何を生み出しているのか、社会で何を引き起こしているのか、感じ取っていたいからだ。それは、目の前の合奏がうまく行っているかどうかを聴き分けている感覚に近い。

この新型コロナウィルス騒ぎが始まってから、政府や行政、そしてテレビなどのメディアは、やたらに「自粛」という言葉を繰り返してきた。やがて誰も彼もがオウムのように「自粛、自粛」と口にするようになってしまった。言葉という音は、僕たちの思考や関係を常に形作っている。無意識に無疑問に、ただ使うということは、実はとても危ういことでもある。

「自粛」という言葉はそもそも、社会・第三者から見て「自分の方に、罪や落ち度がある」場合に使う言葉で、その罪や落ち度を認めた上で「自分で自分に、罰や制限を与える」というニュアンスを含んでいる。

店を開かない、活動しない等の「自らに課す制限」はそれに当たる。しかしこの言葉を、普通に社会活動をして暮らす人々に対して使ってしまったら、「普通に社会生活をすることが罪」「普通に働き、稼ぎ、人と関わり、人とつながりながら国民生活をすること自体が、罪と成り得る」という意味になってしまう。

これでは、多くの人が自分の暮らしそのものに胸を張れなくなり、不必要な罪悪感を抱く場合だって起こり得る。また逆に「自粛しない者＝罪の自覚が出来ぬ者たち」という風に受け取って、一方的な正義を振りかざし他人に鉄槌を与えようとする、歪んだ思考の人々が出て来るのも無理はない。悪者探しよろしく、勘違いな愚行に及ぶ自粛警察などが巷を跋扈(ばっこ)してしまう結果になるのは、少し考えたら分かることだ。

これは今の日本社会が、言葉に敏感でない者たち、日本語に無知な者たちに振り回されてしまっていることを示している。多少なりとも日本語について知っている人間がいるならば、「自粛」ではなく、「自重」と言い直すべきだった。「まだこのウィルスに関しては、分からないことが多すぎるので、もう少し状況が見えてくるまで、自重してください」「お互いに、自重しませんか」と、まずは呼びかけるべきだった。

自重とは何かを、説明すべきだった。情報を共有し、信頼関係を築こうとすべきだった。

不安を軸にした判断は、大概誤っている。これはそれこそ、歴史を見れば明らかだ。自粛要請などという意味不明の言葉を突き付けられて、仕事がなくなった人、仕事を捨てざるを得なかった人、鬱になってしまった人々は大勢いる。ただでさえ多かった自殺者は、このコロナ禍において更に増えている。政府や行政・メディアだけでなく、言論者の顔をしている人々までが、右に倣えして「自粛」という言葉を行き交わせていたが、これこそウィルスよりも厄介なウィルスではなかったのだろうか。誰も自重と言い直さないし、自制や自律という言葉も、ほぼ使おうとしない。与えられた言葉で思考し、関係を築こうとするのは、創造的とは言えない。言葉は、人を救いもするし、追い詰めもする。

言葉に敏感になるということは、とても重要なことだ。「自粛」という言葉の音や意味に、暗く重いものを感じていた人は、せめて「自重」という言葉を使うようにして、自分自身の力と思考を取り戻して欲しい。お互いに思いやり、気遣い、賢明であろうとするならば、「自重」でいい。そしてそれは、「させられる」ものではない。お互いの不安を取り除こうとすること、気遣おうとすること、それは助け合いたいという想いがあってのものだから。自粛要請などを求めるような社会は、人々の中に「自重できる強さ」を育むことは出来ないだろう。

岩井昭（日本・岐阜）

蛍光灯

天井から吊り下がっている
蛍光灯のヒモを
手さぐりで引っ張る
消えて　点く
何度もくりかえす
糖尿病を永く患っていた父の眼は
もうみえないのだろう
ヒモを引っ張る
命が消えるように
間をおいて点く
光　と　闇
生　と　死

何か必死にいおうとする
父の口元に耳を近づけても
何がいいたいのか
もう　わからない

二日後に
父は逝った
謎解きの宿題を
ぼくにのこして

Akira Iwai (Japan/ Gifu)

Fluorescent Light

Hanging down from the ceiling,
A string of a fluorescent light.
Pulling down it, groping for it,
My father lights it on and off,
Which he repeats many times.
He cannot see any more,
He suffered from diabetes for long.
He pulls the string,
It takes some time to light,
When his life seems to vanish.
Between light and darkness.
Between life and death.

He tries to say something with all efforts.
I put my ear down closest to his mouth,
I cannot hear no more,
What he wants to say.

In two days,
He passed away.
Leaving to me,
A puzzle, for my homework.

(Translator: Noriko Mizusaki)

メリーの樹

月桂樹の苗を畑の隅に植えた
その下で
首輪をはずしたメリーが横たわり
やがて土に帰っていく

中学生になった息子が
もの心つくかつかないかに
家に来たビーグル
今まで
共に過ごしてきたが
犬小屋にはもういない

共有する時間が永遠にこない
そのことに気づいたとき
ふれあった歳月が
思い出としてかたりづくられていく

一年もたてば
家族以外のだれもが
メリーとう名の犬がいたことも
忘れるだろう

メリーの樹と名づけた
月桂樹の木かげで
どんな物語がはじまろうと
ぼくらは知ることさえできないが
いまはささやかな由来を
語りつごう

Merry’s Tree

I planted a young sapling of a laurel tree,
In the corner of my field.
Under the tree,
Merry a dog is lying,
With her collar removed.
She will go returning to soil.

My son took her, a beagle dog, so young, to our home.
It was when he was a student of his middle high school.
We were living together with her,
But she is not in her kennel any longer.

Years when we lived together would not come back forever,
When we realized it,
The years we touched together started to be,
Formed into a kind of a memory.

In a year everyone will forget.
Even a fact that a dog named Merry,
Once lived with us, except for my family.

Under a shadow of the laurel tree,
That I named Merry’s tree,
What kind of a story will start,
We cannot even know.
But now I am telling down to you,
On a small life story of Merry.

(Translator: Noriko Mizusaki)

岡山晴彦（日本・東京・熊本）
Haruhiko Okayama (Japan/ Tokyo/ Kumamoto)

短歌五首
Five Tanka Poems

蜂の来るまゆみ花散る聖五月女王の卵かがやきていむや
In holy May, bees coming, blossoms of the bow tree fall
Eggs of the Queen bee may shine bright, may they not?

なんとなく人を嫌ひて青い目の人形と港の風車に会ひにゆく
I do not know why, but avoiding and disliking humans
I go out to see blue-eyed dolls and a windmill in the port.

翡翠の嘴上ぐる天の声未知なるものの美しとおもふ日
A kingfisher raises his beak up: hear the heaven's voice,
On the day when I think what unknown is all beautiful.

さまざまの祈りを見きや狛犬のまなじり伝ひ梅雨は滂沱と
Did he see various prayers? At the gate of the shrine sitting,
A guardian dog : rain drops down from his eyes like a river.

噴き上げははや冬の色ベンチにて修道院に入りし文読むわれは
A fountain tinted so early of the winter color, on a bench I see,
Then read a letter on entering a nunnery I do, doing it I am.

(Translator: Noriko Mizusaki)

近況

今号には、山本代表への献詩を寄せたが、詩集『相：抄と鈔』の第一章「鳥」、『水の充実』の第一章「鳥族の交信」は、正に今のコロナ波乱を思わせ、詩人に与えられた天啓の予知を感じることであった。

今月は童話集六編（原稿二百枚）の大凡まとめ上がった。中に「春の海　少年とバイオリン」という作品がある。NHKテレビの『にっぽんの芸能』はよく見ているが、五月に義太夫狂言の三大名作の一つ『菅原伝授手習鑑』の「寺子屋」の段があり、この童話とのからみもあり、頷く場面があった。なお昨年は早稲田大学の講座（演劇博物館　児玉竜一教授）でこの作品を一年がかりで学んだこともある。童話の中に菅原道真公が太宰府の筑紫（大宰府）に左遷されたとき、愛していた三本の木の中、櫻は悲しみで葉を落とし枯れ、松は途中で力尽きそこで根を下ろし、梅だけは京から筑紫まで飛んできたという伝説に触れている。テレビで芝居の主要な人物の松王丸、梅王丸、桜丸の役柄がこの伝説によっているのが分かり、江戸の原作者の意図に触れることができ、童話とも合わせ嬉しかった。

なお、五月には、今後の励みになるよう、『日本劇作家協会』に入会した。

（山本十四尾主宰「衣」49号より、2020年7月発行）

解説

岡山晴彦氏の熊本地震と『今様お伽話』の七五調使用

水崎野里子

岡山晴彦氏の演劇関係の出版にはまず『女鳥』（2016）がある。氏は詩劇を狙う戯曲作者である。「Pegada」同人でもあり、氏の新作戯曲の発表が「図書新聞」3362号、志村有弘氏の同人誌時評で冒頭に取り上げられた。戯曲童話として紹介の『今様お伽話　麦の穂』(「Pagada」第19号)である。登場は山に住むネズミ(ネズ吉)、山の粉ひき小屋に住む又六爺、町の廃校に住むネズミ、老猫の虎三、その猫を飼っている少年春夫と母、ネズ子。そして背景には「七年前の大地震」がある。ネズ吉は又六爺に教えられ、貨物電車に乗って町へ行く。町での経験がドラマとして展開し、大地震で父を失い、祖父が行方不明の少年春夫や虎三、廃校に住むネズミたちなどに出会い、ドラマが進行し、最後に又六爺が行方不明の春夫の祖父と判明し、ネズ吉は廃校に住む町のネズミと「友情の絆」を結び、最後にはネズ子を嫁に迎えて山へ帰る経緯が、一貫した七五調のセリフで綴られる。

「七年前の大地震」とは、熊本大地震ではないか？当時、直下型大地震により熊本市と熊本城はバラバラに破壊された。その現実の中から、廃校に住むネズミたちによる「友情の絆」が、同じく廃校に住んだ被災者たちによる、復興と立ち上がりのための連帯の比喩として子供用にやさしく説明されている。ちなみに岡山氏は熊本出身である。立ち上がりを祈る、氏の故郷への思いが、子供のための童話劇の形を取りつつ熱っぽく語られた。

だが、本劇が宿す問題はそれだけではない。本戯曲についてはもうひとつ付け加えたい。本戯曲は七五調で書かれている。これは凄い！との感激と驚きが、本誌に再度、今度は短歌ご寄稿をお願いした理由でもあった。

一時(いっとき)、喜劇は散文で書かれると言われていた。だが、モリエールはアレクサンドランという音節リズムの定型行で書き、またW.B.イェイツはファルス(狂言)『三月の丸い月』をブランクヴァース(弱強五脚)で書いている。岡山氏の喜劇七五調の音楽性には、さすが熊本！との称賛もある。同じく熊本出身の劇作家、木下順二の一連の詩劇として書かれた、民話劇(散文)の定型を破る、あるいは補った、ユニークな試みである。

木下順二はシェイクスピアを初めとして詩劇を追求したが、詩劇の要因のひとつとして、アイルランドの詩人・劇作家が着目した民話性を重視した。あるいは、これもアイルランドの劇作家シングに習い、方言使用を詩劇構造として展開した。喜劇性には、狂言役者を起用した。他方、岡山氏は詩劇に、民話性ではなくむしろ童話性を導入し、新たに七五調リズムの音楽性を乗せた。民話と方言には依拠しなかった。新たな詩劇を創造したことになる。

詩劇性に七五調を使用した、これは画期的であり、見事である。このことは最後になるが、日本のいわゆる＜戦後期（第二芸術論）＞による、詩歌戯曲の世界的レベルからの落ち込みを補うものとして特筆する。本作を喜劇として発表した（シェイクスピア喜劇のように悲喜劇性をもちつつ最後は結婚のハッピー・エンドで終わる構造である）、氏の世界戯曲のたゆまぬ知識と勉学にも最後に言及したい。拙学ながらも書評を書かせていただいた。

木下順二のシング寄りの民話劇と詩劇論を補填する、あるいは変革を含めつつ継承する新しい日本の詩劇が、同じく熊本に住んだ文学者によって生まれた。

吉田健一（日本・大阪）

異邦の海辺で

異邦の海辺で
私は一人大きな網を打つ

そして一人　網を引く

長い長い　白い砂浜

鳥も無い　船も無い

けれど　海は凪ぎ渡っている

空いっぱい
私は網を広げる

時が過ぎ

海面を見つめて
私は一人網を引く

魚は少し
死体は二つ

収穫を感謝し
いつものように
私は祈る

Kenichi Yoshida (Japan/ Osaka)

On a Seacoast of a Foreign Country

On a Seacoast of a foreign country,
I am alone, throwing away a big net.

And I am alone, pulling it back.

The coast is long, so long, and white.

No birds I see, nor any ships.

Yet the sea is all calmed out.

All over the sky,
I spread the net.

Time passes.

Watching the water surface,
I am alone, pulling the net.

A few fish in my catch,
And two dead bodies.

Appreciating them,
As usual,
I pray to the god.

異邦の海辺で
無縁の死体が
乾いて消える

On the seacoast of the foreign country,
The unknown corpses,
Dry out, and vanish.

(Translator: Noriko Mizusaki)

水崎野里子（日本・東京）

コロナ垣

出雲なる　雲湧く八重垣
十重二十重
妻と籠もらん
夫と籠もらん

息子命(みこと)の一振りの剣
八重垣切らんか
コロナ垣

（2020年7月15日記）

Noriko Mizusaki (Japan/ Tokyo)

Corona Hedge

In Izumo, clouds well up mountainous.
Into a hedge, eight-folded, many folded.
Confine us together with my husband,
Confine with my wife, ourselves to hide.

Mikoto* my son shall give a swing of sword
Shall he split down the hedge for our liberty.
May we escape out of darkness to our safety,

*Translator's Note: Meaning, a hero or a god, in an ancient Japanese.

*On the 16th of July Noted Down

(Translator: Noriko Mizusaki)

あらたま
NEW BEADS: FOR A NEW YEAR

あらたまの年の初まりしろたへの白衣(ぎぬ)まとひ富士山明けく

Like a new bead,

A new year started:

White silk gown

Heavenly clothing

Mt. Fuji is shining

あらたまの御代(みよ)もみとせ今年こそ和の国さやかに世界へ跳べよ

Like a new bead

Reiwa era is the third

Jump to the world

A country of harmony may

It my wish this year I pray

あらたまの年を迎へてこの世界去年(こぞ)の雪こそ溶けて流れよ

Like a new bead

A new year we welcome

May in this world

The snow of the last year

Thaw into a flowing river

あらたまの年のおほぞらしろたへの雲のたなびき唐衣(からぎぬ)と見ゆ

Iike a new bead

A new year’s firmament floats

The heavenly white

Clouds trailing: thickly woven

Look like a gorgeous silk gown

あらたまの年の初めに汲む水の清(すがし)くありて今年も幸ある
Like a new bead
At the beginning of the year
I ladle up water
It icy: transparent and so clear
We may be blessed also this year.

あらたまの日輪昇りわが里に朝日の満ちて春ぞ来たらむ
Like a new bead
The new year’s sun rising up
My home village
Being filled with the morning light
The new spring has come along just

凍りける湖水も溶けて流れゆくあらたまの春わが身うるほす
The lake water frozen
May dissolve and thaw it away
Into a flowing stream
The spring like a new bead may
Give holy water for me to purify

憎しみもいくさもありしこの世にて和とぞ立ちなむあらたまの春
In this world are
There hatred and conflicts
This very year at last
May it peaceful up stand!
This spring of a new bead

あらたまの年ぞ迎へてわが身古る万歳踊りを君と踊らむ
A year like a new bead

Welcoming: my years got aged
Why not dance with me?
A dance festive in the celebration
Praying for a long life realization

あらたまの年の始まり初夢は宝船ゆく福の神来る
Like a new bead
A new year is beginning
My first dream is:
Treasure ships come sailing
The lucky gods smile coming

(Translator: Noriko Mizusaki)

中尾彰秀（日本・和歌山）
Akihide Nakao (Japan/ Wakayama)

あるがまま(1)
Natural: As I am (1)

今ここに居ながら
遥かなものと一体となる
そのてんまつを恍惚と言うは容易い
他ならぬ古代より古い生命の本質がそうさせている
あ　る　が　ま　ま　に

Now I staying here: I am
Having got unified with something beyond me
It is easily that you call the process the trance
The essence of life long since the ancient age gives me
Be natural: as I am

(Translator: Noriko Mizusaki)

2020年度パンドラ賞発表
植木信子さん

感謝状

植 木 信 子 様

あなたの長年に亘る詩活動と
新潟と東京を往復する精力的
な詩活動に感謝し、ここに賞状
を授与します。あなたはダイナ
ミックな想像力を日本の抒情
詩に付加しました。精力的なそ
の活動に感謝します。

令和二年七月五日

世界詩人会議大阪大会記念

日本会長水崎野里子

藤田晴央（日本／弘前）

雪

ひとつまたひとつと
星のように
あとからあとから
絶え間なく
枯葉のように
くるくると
羽根のように
ふわふわと
私は雪かきをして
疲れ
シャベルにもたれかかり
全身を空に包まれた
山頂の登山者のように
岩のかけらになりながら
空の泉から湧いてくる
あなたを想っている

Haruo Fujita (Hirosaki/ Japan)

Schneeflocken

Erst eine, dann noch eine
wie Sterne
eine nach der anderen
ohne Unterlass.
Sich wie herabfallende Blätter
drehend,
wie Federn
schwebend.
Vom Schneeräumen
ermattet
stütze ich mich auf die Schaufel.
Mein ganzer Körper in den Himmel gehüllt
wie ein Bergsteiger auf dem Gipfel,
werde ich wie ein Fels
und denke an dich,
die du aus dem Quell des Himmels hervorsprudelst.

Übersetzung: Haruo Fujita
Monika Unkel

*Erstveröffentlichung: Yamnashi Nichinichi Simbun 22.Dezember, 2019

岩木山

頂きに立ち
肺いっぱいに吸った青空を蓄えとして
少年は　父のような母のような
山を背にして旅立った

男は流れる雲のような旅からもどり
ふるさとが変わってしまったと嘆いたが
山を仰ぎみているうちに
変わったのは自分だと気づいた

いま　男は　山がその両肩の
黄金の翼をひろげるとき
自分の胸から鳥たちがはばたき
山に帰ってゆくのをみる

男は気づいた
あの町にいてもこの町にいても
わたしは幾たびも
この山に帰っていたのだと

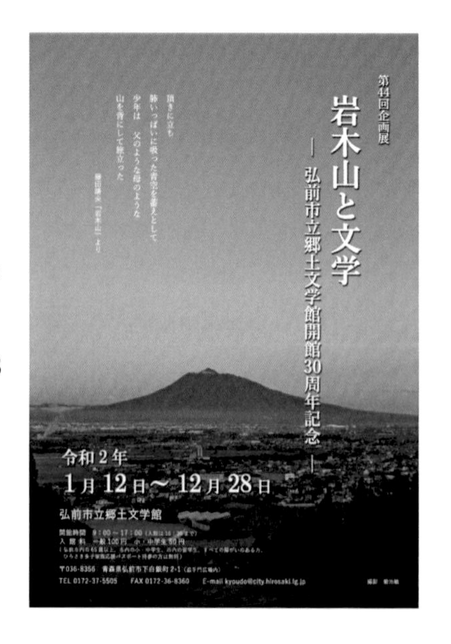

※この詩は弘前市立郷土文学館で開催中の「岩木山と文学」に発表展示されたもの。「岩木山と文学」展は2020年12月28日まで。

Mt. Iwaki

Standing on the top,
Storing the blue air he fully inhaled in,
A boy travelled out with his back turning
From the mountain, which was like his father,
And his mother.

When he returned from his wandering travel
Just like in the flowing clouds,
He deplored that his hometown had changed.
Though, while looking up at the mountain,
He realized that it was himself, not the mountain,
That had changed.

Now when golden wings of the mountain spreads,
He sees from his own bosom birds fluttering up
And go return to the mountain.

He realized one day,
His heart is always coming back
To this mountain wherever he was.

(Translator: Noriko Mizusaki & Haruo Fujita)

*This poem is exhibited in the special exhibition: "The Mt. Iwaki and Japanese literature," in the Hirosaki-shi Literary Museum, from January 12th to December 28th, 2020.

キム・ヨンフン（韓国・ソウル）

ガンジス河の畔にて

生者は　心の迷いを
あの汚れた河の　水とともに　流し去り
そして　信仰に満ちた裸体とともに
芳香を放つ　希望を産み出す

死者は　炎と昇華し
残った亡骸は　河によって育まれ
そして　漂い　沈殿していく
河は　いつも　空の声に　耳を澄ませる

（ハングル翻訳：秋葉信雄）

김영훈 (한국/서울)

다뉴브 여행

근면했던 보상으로 떠난 여행
다뉴브강변 나무들은 춤추는데
무질서가 대고 무참하게 떠밀어
뱃놀이 사람들은 수장되었다

그 강물 바다에서 구름되어
세상 구경하고 돌아오는 길
고향 바다 절벽 노크하던 영혼
먹구름 가슴 천둥쳐 비 내린다

선한 사람이 천사된다는데
산 자와 대화할 수는 없지만
언제나 자유로운 그 영혼들
세상 모든 곳을 여행하리라

다뉴브 강물 말없이 흘러가
밤바다 성나서 울부짖을 때
새벽이 은하를 지우고 나면
승천 몫까지 인생은 일이다.

Young Hoon Kim (Korea/ Seoul)

Dear President Noriko Mizusaki,

I have received your letter.

As COVID-19 is spreading worldwide, I wish for you to stay healthy and take precautions from the disease.

As I am at an old age now, I closed my dental clinic a few years ago, and I am only writing poems in current days. Therefore, my address has been changed to the address written on the envelope.

Thank you for inviting my poem to the literature magazine being published in Japan. I had my poem written in Korean translated into English, but I was not able to have it translated into Japanese. If you know any poet in Japan who is proficient in Korean, and if that poet can translate my poem into Japanese, I would very much appreciate it.

Literature has great power, as it allows us to build friendship beyond borders and language barriers.

I am a member of Korean Society of Authors.

I wish for your health and well-being.

May 2020

Sincerely yours, Young Hoon Kim

原詩夏至（日本・東京）
Shigeshi Hara (Japan/ Tokyo)

俳句
駆け比べ

Haiku
Running Races

春暁の夢より還る閨の闇

Returning from
A dream of spring dawn
Dark is a bed room

春火事に焼けし窓より水滴（みずしずく）

Spring fire burned
A window: from there
Water drops down

寝息ふと乱れ妻醒め朧の夜

Sleeping breadths
Deranged: My wife awoke
Hazy the night

追ひ風といへど春風駆け比べ

Favorable winds yet
Spring winds competitive
Running races

傾いてゐる春天のポールかな

Slanting a pole
Up in the spring sky

春雪に抗ひ愛に抗ふも

Struggling with spring snow
Struggling against love...

紅梅に人群れゐたり風の庭

Red ume blossoms
People gather around
A garden windy

春望や遠富士淡き紫に

A spring landscape
Mt. Fuji afar in a view
Looks pale purple

満開にして花筵なし静寂(しじま)

Stillness around
Cherry blossoms in full
No petals matted

また帰り見む巣は今も花陰に

Wishes to return
To see the full bloom; my nest still
Under the tree

(Translator: Noriko Mizusaki)

草倉哲夫（日本・福岡）
Tetsuo Kusakura (Japan/ Fukuoka)

翻訳：『ハーバースペイの魔法の歌：
ネイティヴアメリカンの歌と詩のアンソロジー』より(2)

山のさえずりの歌（ナバホ）

大地にすばらしさをもたらす声よ
ささやきの中で繰り返される
暗い雲の間に
天国の声のように
声は上へと
大地にすばらしさをもたらす声よ
大地にすばらしさをもたらす声よ
声は下へと
キリギリスの声
低い作物の間に
繰り返されるその音色
大地にすばらしさをもたらす声よ

山の歌は九月の儀式である。病気を治す目的のために異界の力に祈願することを意味した。

ヤクイの歌（ヤクイ）

たくさんのかわいい草たち、赤、青、そして黄色。
ぼくらは少女たちを誘うよ 「さあ　みんな　行こう
花の間を歩こうよ。」
風が花々をゆすっているよ。
少女たちが踊るとまるで花のよう。
広く開いた大きな花々や
ちびっ子の小さな花々もいる。
鳥たちは太陽の光そして星の光を愛している。
花々の香りは甘く。
少女たちはその花々よりもかぐわしい。

山椒魚

半開きのドアの向こうに
若い夫婦と幼子を見た
午後の陽を浴びて
ふくませた乳房が光っていた
おどける犬
おだやかな光景だった

夕方　小さな浴室で
青年といっしょになった
悪性のガンですでに髪はなかったが
まだつややかな肌をしていた

病棟の灯がおち家族が去ると
患者は人気のないロビーに集まる
孤独の長い時間をまぎらわすために
生きていることを暗い笑いで確かめる

ロビーからもどりまぶたを閉じた
むかし好きだった本が思い出された
岩屋に閉じこめられた
『山椒魚』の孤独を愛したことが
にがにがしかった
求めずとも
幼子も青年も私も
すでに岩屋の中だった

（初出「詩人会議」2020年9月号）

Salamanders

Beyond a half opened door,
I saw a young couple and a young baby.
In the afternoon sun,
Shining was her breast, suckled at by the baby.
A dog behaved funny.
It was a peaceful landscape.

In the evening in a small bath room,
A young man stayed with me.
He had no hair because of his cancer's therapy,
He still had a shiny skin, though.

After the patients' wards are lighted and their families leave,,
Patients gather in the empty lobby.
Killing time long and solitary,
They make sure that they are living, by kind of a dark smiling,

Returned from the lobby, I closed my eyes.
A book I once liked reading, I remembered.
I felt it bitter to love the solitude of a salamander,
That was confined in a rock space.
Not seeking for,
The young baby, a young man, and myself,
All have been confined long in the rock space.

*First printed: in *Shijinkaigi*, September Isuue, 2020

(Translator: Noriko Mizusaki)

働淳（日本・福岡）

公園と台風

朝の公園を歩く
木がみきから折れている
気もちも折れそうな
ときおり強い風がふく
夜中にかけ抜けた台風
またつぎの台風がきて
「これまで経験したことがない」とか
「百年に一度」とか
「命を守る行動」とか
くりかえし何度もきく言葉

きずなやつながりと言っていた日常に
亀裂が入ったこの年
まつりや花火や展示にコンサート
人がつくるイベントに代わって
大雨、雷、竜巻、高潮、洪水、地震
と地球のえがくリアルがつぎつぎに押し寄せ
でも怖いのはヘイト（憎悪）に差別に自粛（警察）
身近な人が毎月死んでも
葬儀はなく記憶もうすれて
夜ごと献杯を続けています
人でなく人口が激減していくのです

夕暮れの公園を歩く
不気味な赤い太陽が沈む

Jun Hataraki (Japan/ Fukuoka)

PARK AND TYPHOON

I am walking in the park in the morning.
A tree is broken off the trunk.
As if breaking my senses, too,
Strong winds still come attacking me.
A typhoon dashed through during the night.
Another one will come on us and I shall hear
Such phrases, repeatedly, so many times:
"We have never experienced,"
"Once in these one hundred years," or
"Take actions to protect your lives!"

We used to refer to human links or cooperation,
Yet, this year, splits were caused in our daily days.
Taking place of such events we can organize, as festivals,
Fireworks, exhibitions, and concerts,
Such natural phenomena as, heavy rains, thunders, tornadoes,
High tides, floods, and quakes, rushed to us one after another,
They are realities that our planet Earth has drawn out.
But, the most fearful are, hatred, distinction,
And the self-restraint for the COVID-19, (and the police).
Even when people close to us should pass away
One after another, every month,
We cannot have their funerals. Getting his or her memory faded away,
All we can do is dedicating cups of wine every night.
We should think that a population, not humans, is decreasing,

犬に連れられた人が
スマホで明日の天気を調べている
時おり強い風が吹く
「これまで経験したことがない」できごとが
明日もまた、待っている

In a large number.

I walk in the park, in the evening.
The red sun is setting, looking weird.
A man led by his dog is checking tomorrow’s weather,
In his smart phone.
Now and then, strong winds still come blowing.
Such happenings, as, “we have never experienced”
Will wait for us, tomorrow, too.

(Translator: Noriko Mizusaki)

須藤あきこ（日本・青森）
Akiko Sudo (Japan/ Aomori)

眠れない夜

深夜 病院のベッドで
急に襲ってくる寒さに　目覚め
夢遊病者のように
廊下を　歩いていく

車椅子を　両の腕で
静かに　移動させて行く人と
すれ違う　互いに
暗黙の共感を　感じながら

「あなたは誰？　どこから来たの？」
繰り返される問いが　隣人の眠りを妨げ
個室へ移動させられた方に
平安が　与えられますように

寝返りができず
起き上がることもできず
ただ　呻くしかない人の辛さが
安らかな　眠りに変えられますように

眠れない夜
そっと　見まもり
とりなすことによって
自らも　癒されていくよう

若い身体が……

若い身体が　燃え尽き
老いる　からだを　感じたとき

　　成熟した　精神は　深遠な　知恵によって
　　新しい創造が　はじまる

未知へ　導かれる
喜びと　賛美を　こころに　秘めながら

Scott Watson (USA/ Japan/ Sendai)
スコット・ワトソン（米国 / 日本 / 宮城）

KENJI COUNTRY

Aug. 19 (2010) Monday.

Exit Northeast Turnpike 3 p.m. at South Hanamaki interchange onto route 12. Just onto this local road, a lone withered leaf drops from sky at our approach. Flutters down in front of us.

Then thunder, lightening, and rain hard driven. Wipers can't keep up. Shall we pull off the road?

アメニモマケズ
ame ni mo makezu

Do not be undone by rain

It's the poetry god sending us a message: this is Miyazawa Kenji country.

Temperature drops from 34 (centigrade) to 24. Hallelujah! Hallelujah! Bring a body some relief, poem god.

Aug. 10 Tuesday.

It's seemingly just a coincidence that has us on this day at Kenji's birth site. This day in 1945 the house that was here was burnt down by a conflagration from aerial bombing around Hanamaki Station. The house here now is owned and lived in by descendants of Kenji's younger brother.

Why was Hanamaki bombed? What was here--poor farming area--that needed bombing? Nothing. It's just that the railroad from here to Kamaishi on the coast carried cargo, supplies. So the railroad and the railroad station were targets, and the fire spread from there. This was four days after Hiroshima. Five days before the war ended.

Kenji was dead 12 years before this.

His grave is at a Buddhist Temple. Nichiren sect. Backed by tall cedars. Fresh flowers on his grave.

*****

We're staying at a hot spring. We prepare our own meals in a communal kitchen. We brought along our electric fan from home.

There's a stream rushing by. We can't stay long in the gender-free outside bath because August is "abu" season. Abu means horsefly. They are aggressive. They bite and can leave a big welt. There are five other baths indoors. We go from one to another. These are separated by gender.

rocks rough
water warm
earthly passions

a traveler's shadow
at stream's bottom
free for all

neither rich nor poor
butterfly coitus

One is a heart of soul.
Shed this, shed that

The world's a cauldron
of all that's known.
What's not is a blessing.

Kitakami River.
black damselfly.
Kenji's coat.

World doesn't brake for you
giant dragonfly poem splat

Knowing ourselves
brings us to despair.
Birds know nothing.
Their song gives joy.

A world comes between us.
A poem just is.

Hydrangea, hydrangea
wither, hydrangea

lone crow Kenji
watches rice
fields green.

Kenji's coat
black monarch
butterfly

Walk along the Kitakami River to a place kept named as Kenji called it: English Coast. Because he thought it resembled Dover's cliffs. Kenji had never been to England but had read of it and seen pictures in books.

We're standing barefoot (Morie forgot her walking shoes so I suggested we walk barefoot) taking in the scene. A young couple arrive by car, park at a lot the other side of this embankment. The man says, in Japanese, "So this is the English Coast!" The woman says something apologetically; they leave right away. An elderly fellow who's been tending a garden near the parking lot sees and hears this and watches them pull away. He comes over to where we are and explains why this doesn't look like a coastline anymore. It's not just a tourist gimmick. The river's course has been changed since Kenji's day. This fellow gives us a thirty minute geological explanation which includes our getting our feet wet to see and feel fossilized walnuts lodged in stone underfoot from tens of thousands of years ago. Different from the walnuts of today.

*****

Little birdhouse
in a tree no
world for me

Inextricably
engaged
maple tree me

Thoughts flow away
watching rain

Rain on a tin roof
poem from a friend

MAGIC SHOW

Bliss, order, harmony, Jane,
are in the making, the seeing——
not out there, not in us——
only now

*****

In his youth, a woman at a little Kenji-bilia room tells us, he was regarded by others as a "kawari-mono" (an oddity, different, weird, strange). I ask her how someone goes from oddity to town hero, or the main character of the place. Because in many Japanese cities and towns it's not a poet who holds this position but a feudal samurai lord. Like where I live in Sendai, it's DAH-TE Masamune who is the city's main character. How does a poet get from Kenji the strange to Kenji Bosatsu (Bodhisattva)?

Well, she says, no one realized he would become a famous writer. And then the publishing companies and tourist department do the rest.

*****

We’re off to Kurakake. Saddle Mountain.

Stop for directions at an alpine bathhouse.
We’re told our sandals can’t make the climb.
In comes a mountain nymph
maybe an immortal
in nifty mountain shoes
to walk on clouds.

No one knows roads by route numbers.
Forget your map, mountain ears.

Stop, we’re here.
Happy as hell horseflies
in and out our windows.

Today Saddle Mountain can’t be seen well in mist.
From mountain things won’t be
seen well in mist.
I won’t miss the horseflies.

The heart
of mist is
is
and I’m
growing
old

A man in a camp office shows us photos.
This is like the snow Kenji knows.

MT. KURAKAKE'S SNOW

What you can count on is only
snow covering Kurakake.
Fields and woods,
blotchy with blackness,
are not in the least reliable.
All there is, yeast-like
and but a snowstorm's haze,
with a faint hope to give
is Mount Kurakake's snow.

(An old way's faith)

We take a road back that runs
between Man Mountain and Woman Mountain.
Honk if you want some.

Going On With Basho

From the beginning I want to point out that, because there are various English versions of Basho's masterpiece, each with its own title, I'm going to refer to it in its original Japanese, Oku no Hosomichi.

I'll begin by telling you a little about my reasons and intentions for undertaking a translation of that. Then I'll mention a few points about the translation itself, and, finally, I will offer a personal response to Basho's poetry.

How many here have read Basho in his original Japanese? If you have, you may have experienced some degree of difficulty. The text I used was brought out by a publisher called Shogakukan. In the middle of each page were Basho's own words. At the bottom there was a modern Japanese easy-read explanatory text, and at the top there were notes teaching readers about various people, places, and things Basho mentions. It was rough going for me. It took me three years to read it.

I was in no way prepared. One might say I cut my teeth on Basho's masterpiece. In no way qualified, not a graduate of any Japanese language program, not a student of any famous scholar, without a university degree in Japanese literature, and without any guidance at all, I dove into the deep sea of Oku no Hosomichi.

In my early days teaching at my university, a senior professor called me a "young Turk." According to him, I was angry at everything, criticized everything. Maybe that was my attitude when I took it upon myself to read Basho in the original while looking at someone's English version. By measure of reason, it was not a reasonable thing for me to do, but I was

芭蕉と共に

初めに私は申し上げます。芭蕉の作品についてはいろいろな英語版があり、それぞれの題名で出ています。ですが、私は日本語の原作版、『奥の細道』を基に論を進めます。

私はまず、『奥の細道』の翻訳を始めることになった理由と意図とをお話しします。次に、翻訳自身の持つ問題点を述べ、最後に、芭蕉の作品への個人的な意見を申し上げます。

ここにおいでの何人が、芭蕉を日本語の原作で読んでいますか？　もしお読みになっていたら、いささかの難しさを経験なさったと思います。私が使用したのは、小学館という出版社が刊行したテキストでした。それぞれの頁の真ん中に芭蕉自身の言葉が印刷されておりました。一番下に現代日本語でやさしく読めるように説明が付いていました。一番上には、芭蕉が言及している、さまざまな人々や場所や物事の註があり、読者に教えてくれておりました。その『奥の細道』テキストは、私にはそうやすやすとは読みこなせませんでした。3年かかりました。

それまで、私は準備なるものはまるでしておりませんでした。私は初学者であり、初歩から芭蕉を経験し、基礎から学んでいるとおっしゃる方もおられましょう。資格などありませんでした。日本語コースを修了したわけではありませんし、有名な学者の弟子でもなく、日本文学の学位を取得したわけでもありませんでした。指導も手引きもなく、私は『奥の細道』の奥深い海へと飛び込んだのです。

大学で教え始めた時、私は年配の教授に「怒りんぼ坊主」と呼ばれました。教授によると、私はあらゆることに怒り、あらゆることを批判していたそうです。おそらくそれは、私が、他者による英語版を参照しながら、芭蕉を日本語原作で読むことに挑戦していた時期のゆえと

younger, and maybe because I am American, or maybe just because of the way I am, stubborn, I thought I could do it.

What was it moved me to undertake such an activity? I had seen an English translation of the work way back when I arrived in Japan in 1980. At the time, I was unable to see why Basho is such an important poet. The English seemed nondescript; it did not inspire me in any way. Maybe ten years after that, a man I'd become friends with, an American poet living in Kyoto, advised me to read his version of Oku no Hosomichi. I got that book, published by a small press in America. On one page was the original Basho text. On the facing page was my friend's English version. Although his Japanese was limited, he had a Japanese university professor working with him, so it didn't seem that there would be any issue with the essential accuracy of the translation.

But it was my first look at the original. While struggling to read Basho in his own words, I realized that there is much that had not been brought over into that English language presentation. It was the glory of that first page of the original that inspired me to devote three years of my life to reading the rest. I'm not trying to fault my dear friend's translation. (RIP). But it doesn't get near the original. Nor does my own. No one can. Nor can an easy-to-read Japanese version; compared with the original, it lacks vitality or energy.

Oku no Hosomichi is a magnificent complex organism in which everything connects with everything else, in which each word resonates with homophonous possibility. The haiku are organically connected with the haibun prose. And vice versa.
So that now, 25 years later, if I hear the Yamadera haiku 閑さや岩にしみ入る蝉の声 I am reminded of his haibun. If I hear the haibun. I'm reminded of the haiku. But it also brings back the entire tapestry that is Oku no

思います。まともに考えれば、私がなすべき仕事ではなかったわけですが、私は若く、そしておそらくは私がアメリカ人であったゆえであり、そしておそらくは、私の頑固さが、その難行をやってのけたのです。

いったい何が、私をこの偉業に駆り立てたのでしょうか？　私は1980年に日本に来た時、既に芭蕉を英訳版で読んでいました。でも、私には、なぜ芭蕉がこんなにも重要な詩人であるかまるでわからなかったのです。英語版はなにも語ってはくれませんでした。私に何も霊感は与えてくれなかったのです。それから10年経って、友人となったあるアメリカ詩人が京都に住んでいて、私に彼の翻訳版の『奥の細道』を読むように勧めてくれたのです。私はアメリカの小さな出版社で発行された彼の本を手に入れました。1頁に芭蕉の原作が印刷されていました。見開きの次頁に友人の英語版がありました。友人の日本語はそう流暢というわけではありませんでしたが、彼には日本人の大学教授の同僚がいました。それゆえ、翻訳の基本的な次元での正確さに何らかのクレイムが付くとは思えませんでした。

でも、それは私が最初に見た原作でした。芭蕉を彼の言語（訳者註：元禄時代の日本語）で苦闘しつつ読む経緯で、私は、友人の英語表現では十分にカバーできなかった箇所が結構多いことに気づきました。彼の本の最初の頁の芭蕉の原作のすばらしさが、私の人生の3年間を残りの部分を読むために費やされることになったのです。私は敬愛する友人を批難しようとしているのではありません。そうではなくて、英訳は原作に近づいてはいないのです。私の翻訳もそうでした。誰にも不可能です。また誰にも簡単に日本語原作を読めるわけではありません。原作と比較して、友人の英訳には生命力とエネルギーが欠けていました。

『奥の細道』は壮大で複雑な有機体です。すべてが他のすべてと関連しており、すべての言葉は単一の音声の可能性に向かって響き渡ります。

Hosomichi. One thread contains the entire creation. A universe in a grain of sand. All I can do is sigh, in awe. There are no words. It is a text that, like a Japanese garden, points beyond itself, a finger pointing at a moon, it points a way to, a way of, that mystery that is the Great Beyond, 生と死の源, the source of all our living and dying. But to get to that stage of literary samadhi, one has to put in the work, one has to read the original. No translation will do. If you want the vibes you have "hit the libes" (which is slang from my college days that means go to a library. "Vibes" is short for vibrations, such as in the old Beach Boys' song "Good Vibrations."). Or you can write your own life's journey at depth, using language that resonates with your original universality.

As mentioned, I was young and angry. I was angry because it seemed that some of the English versions were purposely deceiving readers—they weren't, but it didn't seem that way to me then—and, like a small child, I felt sorry for the readers who had no way of telling the translations were so different from the original. I'd fume to myself in my room, and then I'd fume in print: "What is this translator doing?! Basho never wrote that!" "What is this plain, worn out, stale, flat, English style!? Wake up!" I look back now and laugh.

That was my attitude. That's why my version does not appear through any mainstream publisher. That's why no one has ever heard of me. Mine is a mountain hermit's version.

I'm older now. Maybe wiser. Maybe not. Still angry. But now that anger has mellowed.

Now I realize what I was too stubborn to see back then, which is that, like different conductors performing the same piece of music, each translator

構成上、俳句は散文の俳文と相互作用で結びついています。逆も真です。現在、25年後に、もし私が例の山寺俳句、「閑さや岩にしみ入る蝉の声」を聞けば、彼の俳文を思い出します。もし私がその俳文を聞けば、その俳句を思い出します。ですがそれは同時に、『奥の細道』全体のタペストリー（訳者註：風景などを複雑に厚手の糸で織り込んだ絨毯式壁掛け）を連想させてくれます。一本の糸に全体の創造が含まれるのです。宇宙は一粒の砂の中に存在します。私は畏敬の余り、溜め息を付くだけです。もはや言葉は存在しません。それは、日本庭園のように、それ自身を超越したなにものかを指し示しており、月を指し示す指でもあります。それは、生きとし生けるものすべての生と死の源泉に導く神秘の道であり、神秘へ至る道を示しております。ですがその文字通りの「三昧」（訳者註：原語はサンスクリット。瞑想、あるいは精神状態が深まり切った状態）に到るためには、作品に没入し、日本語の原作を読み込まなければなりません。翻訳（訳者註：この場合は英語訳）では理解できません。芭蕉に感銘したいなら、図書館へ行き、日本語の原作を読み込むべきです。あるいは、あなた自身の独自の世界と響き合う言語を使用して、人生の深奥の旅を書くことです。

申し上げたように、若い私は怒ってばかりおりました。腹を立てておりましたのは、英語訳が読者を意図的に騙していると感じていたからです。当時の私にはそう思えました。小さな子どものように、私は読者に申し訳ないと感じておりました。彼等はそれらの訳が原作とは非常に異なるものであるということがわからない人々でありましたからです。私は自分の部屋で腹を立てておりました。次いで、私は文章を印刷して怒りました――「この翻訳者は何をしている？　芭蕉はこんなこと書いてはいない！」、「この、月並みな、使い古しの、陳腐な、退屈な、英語文体は何だ⁉　目覚めろ！」。今思い出しては笑っています。

それが私の怒りの反逆でありました。それゆえに、私の翻訳版はいかなる主流の出版社からも出ないわけであります。だから誰も私に耳を

has her or his individual way to bring out the original. Each, hopefully, has something special to offer.

I think it is important that everyone understand that I am not a Basho expert. I undertook that one task because I was following my spirit, and, after completing Oku no Hosomichi, while that spirit was still with me I translated some 50 or more Basho haiku. After that my spirit took me elsewhere. Just to give you a brief example of what following my spirit means in my life, in my background studies for translating Basho, I was thrilled to read Zhuangzi, the Chinese Daoist sage. Through reading about Daoism I was moved to begin lessons in Tai Chi, and through Tai Chi I became interested in acupuncture and Traditional Chinese Medicine. And, eventually, I brought out a book called Dreaming Zhuangzi. Sometime after the Basho spirit, a student brought some poems by Santoka to class, and I've been involved with Santoka for 20 years.

Here, because it connects with what I was attempting with my own translation, I'd like to quote a passage about Basho from Ueda Makoto's book about him. In his chapter about haibun, readers are told that "... the word haibun means haiku prose, a prose piece written in the spirit of haiku. ... A haibun has... the same sort of brevity and conciseness as a haiku. ...Because of this brevity, the writer is as concise as possible, avoiding unnecessary words; in fact, he often omits words that would be necessary in normal syntax. Although this is not evident in English translation, the predicate verb of a sentence is sometimes left out, leaving the reader to supply it by himself." [121~122]

Let me repeat what was the most important part for me: "Although this is not evident in English translation." What I wanted to do is make what is not evident evident.

貸さないのであります。私の英語翻訳は山の隠者の書き物でした。

今、私はもう若くはなくなりました。おそらくはより賢くなりましたはずです。でも、いまだに腹を立てております。若かった怒りは今、少し丸くなりました。

今私は、当時を振り返り、かつての私は頑固すぎたと考えています。多様な指揮者が同じ曲を多様に指揮するのと同じく、それぞれの翻訳者は、彼なり彼女なりの個人的な視点で原作を解釈しています。それぞれが、何か特有なものを提示しているのです。私はそう希望してそう考えています。

誰もが、私は芭蕉の専門家ではないと理解していることは重要だと考えます。私が芭蕉の『奥の細道』英語訳の仕事に向かったのは、私の霊に従ったまでです。そして、『奥の細道』英訳を完了した後も依然として、その霊はいまだに私と共にあり、50句かそれ以上の芭蕉の俳句を訳しました。それ以後、私の霊は私を他の場所に連れて行きました。読者に手短かにお話しますと、私の芭蕉研究、あるいは芭蕉俳句の成立背景の研究の中で、私は心躍らせて荘子を読みました。中国の道教の賢者です。道教についての書物を読みながら、私は太極拳の練習を始めました。対極拳を通して私は鍼療法と伝統的な中国医術に興味を持ちました。ついには、私は『荘子を夢見る』という本を出版しました。また、ある日一人の学生が教室に山頭火の句をいくつか持って来てくれました。そして、私は山頭火と20年間付き合うことになったのです。

私が芭蕉の翻訳に伴って試みたことと関連しているので、上田真氏*[1]の芭蕉についての本からの引用を申し上げます。俳文についての章の中で、氏はこう述べています──「俳文の意味は、散文の俳句ということである。俳句の精神で書かれた散文の作品である。俳文は、俳句と同じ簡潔さと無駄のなさを持つ。それゆえに、作者は、余計で説明

It was my thinking that, since there were already translations that attempted to find that happy middle ground between a literal translation and a literary translation, a more literal translation might be appreciated by some offbeat reader somewhere. My version has been criticized as a word for word translation. Someone else said that my translation needs a translation. My purpose was to make an English haibun version complete with the gaps and leaps Ueda Makoto mentions, an English haibun that doesn't read like the English prose style we might find in a newspaper article. And I wanted to present Basho in an English that was as rough as Basho's journey. I wanted words through which readers can feel the steps and breathe the physical exertion.

As far as the haiku, instead of explanatory translation, my own tended to use less words and so less syllables than a haiku, and they are in fact not intended as haiku—with the various conditions to be satisfied—but rather they seek to release the spirit of haiku, which is of course inexpressible. Here again, as example, is the one at Yamadera with my English version:

閑さや岩にしみ入る蝉の声

Stone
distills
stillness
cicada
chant

My efforts succeeded: my version is not a smooth read. It's rough going. And in being a success, it's also a failure. No matter how choppy, distorted, and disconnected my English haibun might seem, it still doesn't capture Basho's magnificence.

的な言葉を出来る限り避ける。作者は、しばしば通常の構文では必要であるような語を省く。この経緯は英語の翻訳においては明らかではないが、文の中の術語動詞はしばしば省略され、自力での補填は読者に任されている。」

以上の引用の中で私に一番重要な部分を繰り返し申し上げます――「これは英語訳では明確には示されていない」。私が成し遂げたかったことは、明確ではないものを明確にすることでした。

私の考えは、逐語訳と文学的な訳の間の、幸せな中間地域を見つけようと試みた翻訳は既に数多く出ています。それゆえ、より逐語訳的な翻訳の方が読者に喜ばれるのではないかということでした。私の翻訳は逐語訳であると批判されて来ました。私の翻訳には翻訳が必要であると言う人もいました。私の目的は、英語版の俳文部分には、上田誠氏が言うように、脱落と跳躍により完成させることでした。英語訳の俳文は、新聞記事に見るような英語散文のように読まれてはなりません。私の願望は、芭蕉を、彼の旅に見るような、山あり谷ありの英語文体で表現することでした。私は、芭蕉の旅という肉体的な行使、その足取りとその呼吸とを読者がまざまざと感じることが出来るような英語を望んだのです。

芭蕉の俳句の英語訳に関する限り、私は、説明的な訳ではなく、より少ない語と、普通の俳句よりもはるかに少ない音節とを使用しております。それゆえ、私の訳は、様々な条件を満たすべく書かれた種の俳句を意図してはおりません。むしろ、表現不可能な、俳句の精神の解放を求めた、そう言った方がよろしいと思います。ここで再び、例として、山寺での芭蕉の句の私の英語訳をお読みください。

閑さや岩にしみ入る蝉の声

To give you an example of what the difference is, my version does not use the word "I." Ever. That is in keeping with the original. Another translator's version has the word "I" a dozen times, and that's only on the first page. "I this," "I that," and so on.

So, having described my reasons and intentions, let me give you a brief and easy example of the great difficulty in trying to translate Basho. Let's start at the beginning, with the very first haiku.

Let's take the Japanese "hina no ie" from the first section of Oku no Hosomichi.

草の戸も　住みかはる世ぞ　雛の家
Kusa no to mo sumikawaru yo zo hina no ie

For the last segment of that haiku, most English versions leave a reader with "a doll's house" or a reference to a "doll festival." Stubborn me, I tried to find a word that might have some connections similar to the Japanese word "hina," which brings in "small," "cute," "endearment," and, like the word "hina," also connotes a baby chickens, or chicks. So, after a painstaking search through one dictionary after another, mulling over words such as teeny weeny, itty bitty, and so on, I found what seemed just the right word: "chickabiddy." So, here is my version:

Thatched hut too, changes
with the world to a home for
chickabiddy dolls

Having given just a small sample of the difficulty of translation, let's go to my personal response to Basho.

Stone
Distills
Stillness
Cicada
Chant

私の努力は成功しています。そうすらすらとは読めません。ごつごつとしております。成功作であり、失敗作でもあります。たとえいくら途切れ途切れで、歪曲され、ばらばらであるように見えても、いまだに芭蕉の壮大さは捉えてはおりません。

私の英語訳の特異性を一例として申し上げますと、私の訳は「わたし」という語を使用いておりません。一度も。「私」を使用しないことは、原作との歩調を保つことです。翻訳者によっては、「私」という語を何度も使用しています。それも最初の頁だけの使用です。「此の私」、「其の私」等々。

私の道理と意図を申し上げましたので。芭蕉を英訳する場合の付きまとう多大な困難についての例を、簡単に短く申し上げましょう。『奥の細道』の冒頭、最初の俳句から始めます。

日本語での「雛の家」の句を取り上げます。

草の戸も　住みかはる世ぞ　雛の家

この俳句の最後の箇所については、殆どの英訳は、「人形の家」、あるいは「雛祭」への言及を読者にほのめかしております。頑固な私は、日本語の「雛」に関連する類似するような語を見つけようとしました。「雛」の語は、「小さい」、「可愛い」、「愛らしい」という属性を持ちます。そして、同時に、「雛」という語はひよこ、ニワトリの赤子を

325 years have passed since Basho breathed his last poem. His words speak still, speak the stillness. More than three hundred years, and Basho's words are all the brighter. Here we are, more modernly civilized than ever, ever more technologically equipped, though sliding into various modes of collapse and taking, as the United Nations recently tells us, the rest of nature with us.

Basho's poems are guiding lights, natural landmarks bespeaking the commonality of all life. They shine like stars, and this is so relevant to our times, because the world we live in has become so much darker.

Why read Basho now? To ask "why read Basho?" is the same as asking "why breathe?" To stay alive is the only answer I can come up with. In order to survive.

Ours are lives that are given order by flowers, by moon, each imparting to everything else its nature, its spirit, all coming together as one. A harmony.

月華の是やまことのあるじ達
つきはなの　これやまことの　あるじたち

Moon, flowers:
these are true
masters' masters

These "beings"--moon, stars, flowers, mountains, grasses--are true masters. We, our knowing selves, do not make a sense of order, no more than do we grow our own hands. We can only experience an order within us, simply by being as we are.

Had Basho lived longer, how would he have changed? (And he would

意味しています。それゆえ、辞書を次々と引き、探し求め、考えに考えた挙句に、私はまさにぴったりだと思われる表現を見つけました。Chickabiddyです。(訳者註:ピヨピヨ、かわい子ちゃん。Chicaには娘、少女の意味あり、もとはスペイン語。またchickとはひよこ、ひな鳥のことである。Biddyにはニワトリ、ヒヨコという意味と共に、ウルサイババアという意味もあり)。私の英訳は以下です。

Thatched hut too, changes
With the world to a home for
Chika biddy dolls

翻訳の難しさの例を申し上げましたので、次に私の芭蕉への個人的な意見に移ります。

芭蕉が最後の句を書いてから325年が過ぎました。ですが彼の句はいまだに語り掛け、静寂を語ります。300年以上経っても、芭蕉の句はますます輝きます。私たちは今、今まで以上に現代的に文明化され、科学技術の恩恵を受けております。ですが種々の形での崩壊に滑り込んでもおり、国際連合が最近出しましたように、自然と私たちとの共生を受け入れなければならない時代が来ています。

芭蕉の作品は導きの光であり、人生すべてにおける共通性を語り掛けてくれる道標であります。星のように輝いています。それは今、私たちの時代には非常に重要なことであります。現在、私たちが住む世界は暗さを増しています。

なぜ芭蕉を今、読むのか?　その「なぜ読むのか」という問いは、「なぜ息をするのか?」と同じ問いです。生きるためということが、唯一の私が申し上げ得る答えです。生きていくためです。

have changed, as is the way of nature.) He had been looking to poetry as a way of enlightenment, as a way to settle his heart/mind. Towards the end of his life, he tells of being pestered by the need to make a poem. Poetry would not afford him the tranquility he desired. Had he lived a bit longer, would he have realized that being just as he is is enlightenment, that being just as he is means, for him, being a poet, that enlightenment is not a stage attained through poetry, but, as Zen priest Dogen tells us, in the act of seated meditation itself? "Seated meditation" meaning, for Basho, the making of a poem. But Basho seems to have thought tranquility is something else, some stage that he could not attain because he could not put down his brush.

The true "masters," the moon, flowers, mountains, and stars, are as they are because they are as they are. Their substance—to break it down for comprehension by a mind that wants things broken down—is one with their function. They "have their act together." Basho's enlightenment is no different. The substance of his words and the function of his words are one. That is order, that is harmony, that is enlightenment. I call it radiance.

Notes

"cut my teeth on": acquire initial practice or experience of a particular sphere of activity. J. で経験を積む、…から初めて学ぶ

"a young Turk": The term "Young Turk" is now used generally to denote a member of an insurgent group within an organization (often, although not always, a political party) advocating change, sometimes radical change, in that organization. J. 改革を求める急進派

"nondescript": J. あまり印象に残らない

"samadhi": J. サマーディ．三昧．仏教やヒンドゥー教における瞑想で、精神集中が深まりきった状態のことをいう

私たちが生きることは、花や月に命じられております。それぞれは、他のすべての存在に、自然を、霊を、伝えます。生きとし生けるものは共にひとつの存在と化します。調和です。

月華の是やまことのあるじ達

Moon flowers
These are true
Masters' masters

月、星、花、山、草――これらはまことのあるじです。私たちは、自己を知っていると思っていても、秩序をまるで知りません。私たちはこころの内で秩序を経験していると思っていうだけです。秩序はただ、私たちというあるがままの存在になることによってのみ可能です。

もし芭蕉が長生きしたら、芭蕉はどう変化したでしょうか？（ですが彼は自然のあるがままに生き、変化などしなかったでしょう）。彼は俳句に啓示の道、精神を定着させる道を求めていました。人生の終焉に向かい、芭蕉は書かずにはいられない状況を語っています。彼が望んだ静寂は、俳句は与えてくれなかったのかもしれませんが、もし彼がもっと長生きしていたら、自分こそが啓示であることを悟ったと思います。啓示とは、自分の存在こそが俳人の道そのものであるという認識であります。ですが、啓示に関して言えば、俳句を通して得られる啓示はひとつの段階にすぎず、禅宗の僧侶道元が語るように、座禅の瞑想に啓示はあるのではないでしょうか？　座禅に当たるものは、芭蕉にとっては、俳句を作ることを意味していました。ですが、芭蕉は、座禅の静寂は別物であり、別の修行と考えていたように思えます。なぜなら、彼は筆を捨てませんでした。

「まことのあるじ」である月、花、山、星は、あるがままの存在であり

“Zhuangzi” (Chuang-tsu, 4th century BC). J. 荘子

“offbeat”: J. 風変わり , オフビートの

“Dogen” (1200~1253) Founder of the Soto sect of Zen Buddhism. J. 道元禅師

“have their act together”: 効果的に行動している

ます。なぜなら、それらはあるがままの存在であるからであります。それらの実体は、機能を持つ実体であります。破壊好きな者によって、理解するために必要な破壊の対象ともなり得ます。それらは総合的なひとつの実体です。芭蕉の啓示も変わりません。芭蕉の句の実体と機能はひとつです。それは秩序であり、調和であり、啓示であります。私はそれを光と呼びます。
(2019年9月開催の「世界俳句大会」において英語版発表。於東京神田学士会館)

註*1：上田真。上田 真（うえだ まこと、1931年5月20日－）は、日本文学研究者で、スタンフォード大学の日本文学名誉教授。兵庫県生まれ。1962年ワシントン大学大学院博士課程修了。トロント大学教授、のちスタンフォード大学教授。日本の詩歌が専門で、特に俳句や短歌、川柳について多くの著書がある。比較文学でPh.D.を取得（1962年）。

著書：Matsuo Basho: The Master Haiku Poet (1970)、他多数。

（日本語訳：水崎野里子）

ユ・ハンギュ（韓国・ソウル）

出逢い（詩）1

向かい合うと
いつでも
胸は
ときめいて

かすみゆく
心の中を
燃やしつくしたり
しみわたったり

美しい
言葉の
釣瓶で
想い出を
紡ぎあげて

星たちではなく日の光が
お前と出逢えば
水のような霧とも
なった

消え失せる
日々も
扶助しながら

Yoo Hangyu (Korea/ Seoul)

만남 (시) 1

마주하면
언제나
가슴은
뛰고

아몰어가는
부위에
사르락
스며든다

정갈한
언어의
두레박으로
추억을
잣아올리고

별잣아닌일들이
너를만나면
물안개가
된다

스러지는
널
부축하며

時として
五色の
爆竹と
なって

パンパンと
喜びの香煙
空に高く
音は
昇っていった

（日本語翻訳：秋葉信雄）

때론
오색의
폭죽이
되어

팡팡
기쁨의향연
하늘높이
소리
올린다

(Translator: Nobuo Akiba)

郡山直（日本・奄美喜界島・神奈川）

詩のパン

経験という粉と
インスピレーションという酵母菌を
混ぜて
愛情をこめて
よくこねなさい
それから　力いっぱい　たたいて
しばらく放っておきなさい
それが自分の内側からの力で
大きく、ふくらんでくるまで……
それから　再びこねなおして
丸い形にして
あなたのハートの
オーヴンで
焼きなさい

註
郡山直先生の英語詩は七篇、米国、カナダ、オーストラリア、南アフリカの学校教科書に掲載されている。上記の詩はその一篇である。知る人ぞ知るが、先生のお人柄もあり、あまり日本国内では喧伝されていないのでここにまずはその二篇を再録する。（水崎記）。

Naoshi Koriyama

(Japan/ Amami-Kikaijima/ Kanagawa)

A Loaf of Poetry

You mix
the dough
of experience
with
the yeast
of inspiration
and knead it well
with love
and pound it
with all your might
and then
leave it
until
it puffs out big
with its own inner force
and then
knead it again
and
shape it
into a round form
and bake it
in the oven
of your heart

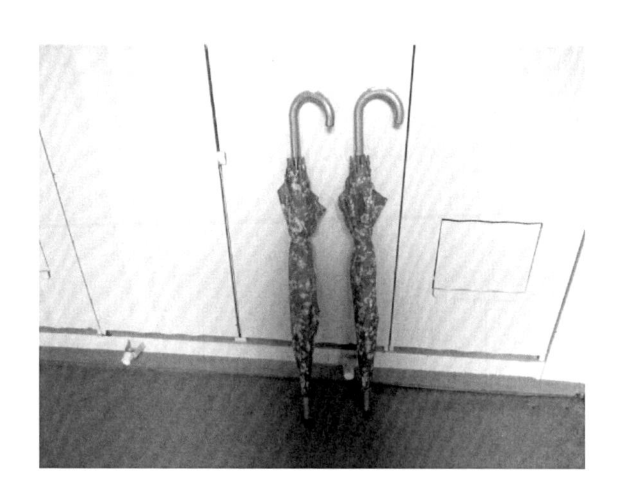

*Quoted from *A FRESH LOAF OF POETRY FROM JAPAN* (2018, BookWay)

*Editor's Note: It is known that the Professor's seven poems were published for teaching texts of poetry in schools for young people, in the Professor's own English: in such countries as USA, Canada, Australia, and the Republic of South Africa. This poem, published above, is one of them.

(Translator: Naoshi Koriyama)

郷里の島の夏

砂糖きび畑の
なかを通っている

岡の道で
男は自転車を止める

そして自転車から下りて
ぞうりを脱ぎ

はだしの足と
剥き出しの心で

郷里の島の土の
感触を感じとるのだ

郷里の島の太陽に焼かれた
土の温もりを感じとるのだ

岡を眺め
海の音を聞きながら

SUMMER ON THE HOME ISLAND

the man stops his bicycle
on the hillside road

that runs through
the sugarcane fields

and he gets off the bicycle
and takes off his sandals

to feel the texture
of his home islands' earth

to feel the warmth of the earth
heated by his home island's sun

with his bare unshod feet
with his free naked heart

looking over the hill
listening to the sound of the sea

*Quoted from *A FRESH LOAF OF POETRY FROM JAPAN* (2018, BookWay)

*Editor's Note: It is known that the Professor's seven poems were published for teaching texts of poetry in schools for young people, in the Professor's own English: in such countries as USA, Canada, Australia, and the Republic of South Africa. This poem, published above, is one of them.

(Translator: Naoshi Koriyama)

長津功三良（日本・岩国）

堕ちた日

原爆が落ちた日にゃぁねや
ちょおど　学校から帰りよったいや
空襲だか　警戒警報だか　だされちの
朝礼だけじ　今日はもお　かえっちええちゆうことになっちの
学校の下の永井商店とこを歩きよったのいや
ピカッと　空一杯にしろおなるよぉに　ひかっちの
そいから　ちいとしてから　どぉんと　きたのいや
周りのやまが　ぐらぐらくるよぉな感じでの
つれち帰りよった下級生の女の子なんかぁ　泣き出しちの

永井とこの前に　長屋みとぉな小屋があっつろうが
そこい　逃げ込んだのいや　小母さんが
せわぁないけえ　心配しなさんな
ちゅうて　おいたのを思えちょるい

おらあ　あの日にゃぁ　熱うだしちの
家じ　寝ちょったのい
へやが　ぱぁっとあかるう光ったとおもったら
ちいっとしち　障子がぐらぐらゆれよるのい
近所い　爆弾でも落ちたんか　おもぉたいや

おらぁ　どぉなんじゃろぉか
家の風呂場のねきで　兔小屋の寝藁かえよったのい
ピカッと　きたのいや　そいで　ちいとしてからに
そこらが暗ろぉなるよぉな感じで

Kozaburo Nagatsu (Japan/ Iwakuni)

On the Day When the A-Bomb Dropped

You see, on the day when the bomb dropped.
I was just on the way from school returning home.
The air raid or precautionary warning was alarmed out,
So only with a morning assembly, they had let us go home.
When I walked by Nagai Store just close from the school,
There came the PIKA! It flashed covering all of the sky white,
Then in some seconds came the thundering sound. DON!
I felt like the surrounding mountains all sway and tremble.
The young girl student I took homeward with me, started crying.

In front of Ngagi's, there was a hut like a row house,
We went escaping into it. Aunty told us that
We should take it easy and should not worry,
Which I remember now.

On that day I had a temperature and
At my home I was lying on a bed.
As soon as I saw the room shine bright in a flash,
Then the paper doors started swaying to and fro.
I thought in my neighborhood bombs might have dropped.

What had become of me?
I was replacing the straw bed for rabbits in the hutch
Beside our bathroom, when the flash came on,
And soon it seemed turned pitch-dark around me.

向かいの城山が　揺れたのい
あのこらぁ　五年生じゃっつろぉ
よぉおぼえちょるいや　喰うもなぁなぁし
何処かの成り物を　喰うしかなぁけぇ
よその山のもん　盗っちゃぁ　追わえられたぃ
おれらぁも　悪かったけぇ　よぉ怒鳴りこまれたいや

そいで　岩国の陸軍燃料廠がやられち
兄貴らぁ　こんだぁ　ひろしまぁへ　救援にいかされてち
堕ちたあくるん日から　五日もおったのい
はぁみい　いまでいゃぁ
残留放射能ちゅうのに　やられちしもうち
酷いもんじゃ　あくるんとしの夏まで
蛆虫だらけじ　暑い　暑い　ちゅうて
苦しみ抜いち　死んだぃや
まだ　はたちにも　なっちょらんだで

Mount. Shiro opposite my house swayed.
At that time I was in the fifth grade of the elementary school.
So I remember it well. I had no foods then,
I could do nothing but eat fruit or vegetables of others' mountains.
Every time I stole something to eat at others' mountains
I was driven away. We were bad boys, I knew. We were scolded away. often.
The Army Fuel Depot in Iwakuni was air-raided and destroyed.
So my elder brother with others were sent to Hiroshima to help them.
He stayed in Hiroshima for five days, since the day.
Yes, you see, in the words for the present we may say,
He was killed by the residential radioactivity.
It was too pitiful. Till the next summer
He was full covered with maggots and kept complaining,
"It's hot. It's hot."
He had suffered from pain, till he passed away,
When he was less than twenty years old.

(Translator: Noriko Mizusaki)

きみよみたか

きみは　みたか　ひろしまを

きみは　いったか　ひろしまへ

きみ　ぜひ　たのむ　ひろしまへ

駅前の集落だったところが再開発されて　百貨店が進出する
駅裏東練兵場へ続く野っ原は　新幹線口のターミナルになった
半世紀経つと　世の中変わるさ

戦争の傷痕は　いま　何処にも見当たらない
しかし　ひとらは　傷痕を隠し　ひっそりと生きている
語り部は少なく　生き残ったことの哀しみを抱いて　沈黙する

戦後のバラックなど　とうに建て替えて　最新式集合住宅になり
道路も　拡幅され　付け替えられ　微かな記憶に　少しずれる
新しい橋も架けられ　車が行き交う
いま繁栄の新世紀に向けての　人口百二十万の政令都市

あの日　女学生たちが　救護所を求めて　集まった　**饒津神社**のあたり

DID YOU SEE IT?*

Did you see Hiroshima?

Did you go to Hiroshima?

Surely, I request you to visit Hiroshima.

The area of the barracks in front of the station had
A redevelopment project.
Department stores came built up.
The field of grass led to the training ground for soldiers,
Turned to a terminal on the exit of the Super Express Station.
You know, in half a century, things changed and replaced.

No scar marks of the war can be seen anywhere, now.
But the people are living quietly, with the scars hidden.
Quite a few are there now storytellers.
Holding their sadness that they survived,
They keep silence, with no speaking out.

The barracks hurriedly made up just after the war
Were destroyed and reconstructed so long ago
Into the modern apartments in the latest fashion.
The roads were reconstructed to the wider, or replaced.
They are a bit different from the slightest memory left for me.
New bridges were also built and on them cars go drive back and forwards.
Now, for the new century of prosperity, the city is a government designated city.

高架を新幹線が疾走する
駅からビルの連なり

記憶を辿るのが　愚かなのか
風化は　当然なのか
この　こころのなかの　影たちの　叫びは
薄れていくのか　いまのうち　ひろしまの　空
　気を吸ってくれ

きみよ　ひろしまを　みたか

きみよ　いまのうち　ひろしまに　きてくれ

きみよ　きおくに　きざんでくれ

きみよ　ひろしまを　みたか

With a population of one million two hundred thousand.

Around Nigitu Shrine, where on the day girl-students
Gathered looking for the first-aid station, you can see
The super express trains dash on the overpass,
Buildings are lining along from the station.

It is a stupid act to trail memories back? Or
The weathering out is natural?
These shouts of shadows in their minds go
Fading away? Before they not have faded out,
Inhale you the air of Hiroshima, can you?

You saw Hiroshima, did you?

You come to Hiroshima, before not too late, do you?

You inscribe it in your memory, do you?

You, have you seen Hiroshima, have not you?

(Translator: Noriko Mizusaki)

広島にて

　橋上に立てば、対岸のドームが見える。
　赤い落陽を受け、聳り立つ不吉な鉄骨と、散りしいた煉瓦の影、さびれた貸ボート場の桟橋と安バラックのペンキの匂いを嗅ぐ。
　その時、俺やおまえ達の、予約された死の意味を聴いた。河底の砂と、砂に埋る白骨の群れに。

俺の生まれた家の記憶、隣家の可愛い少女の記憶。それらはすでに辿るべき形態(すがた)の破片(かけら)すらも無く、ただ足下に満潮の川があるばかり。

　間近い夜の中へ傾斜してゆくドームの、虚しい記憶の重みが、俺のこころを冷たく、呑み込む。

　ああ橋上を風が吹く。
　はげしく地軸の揺れる日の予告(しらせ)であるのか、対岸のドームは、俺の視界で、次第に怪しい燐光を放ちはじめていた。

At Hiroshima

Standing on the bridge, I can see the dome on the opposite bank.

The steel frames soaring up. They looked ghostly in the red setting sun. The bricks broken scattered over on the ground. I see the pier for the boat rental hut left empty. I smelled of the paint on the cheap barracks.

At that time, I sensed what the death is, which had been reserved, for us.

I sensed it from the sands of the river bed, and from the piles of the white bones, which were buried in the sands.

I remember my house where I was born. I remember a lovely girl
who lived next door to us.
They have now no forms to be trailed even in pieces. All I have got is the river at high tide, flowing at my foot.

The doom is slanting into the night approaching. The weight of the vain memory gulped me down in the coldness.

Oh, on the bridge winds blow.

It may be a forecast for the day when the earth's axis has terrible shakes? The dome on the opposite side of the river has started shedding white light in phosphorus, which looks weird, in my sight.

(Translator: Noriko Mizusaki)

市川ツタ（日本・茨城）

恵送手製詩葉書より(1)
生きる

自粛は禁止ではない
禁止に近いが
食べるものの買い出し　通院は
この限りでないという
マスク　消毒　手洗い
人との距離2メートル厳守
それらを守って出来るだけ早く
用事を済ませ帰宅
うがい　石鹸で指先　手首まで
丁寧に洗い
見えないコロナに抵抗する

歩くこと不可　重いもの持てず
食べぬわけには行かず
我慢の最少活動範囲で
事故と転倒気を付け
明日も生きると
前だけを見る老いの一途さ

（2020年7月9日ご送付）

Tsuta Ichikawa (Japan/ Ibaraki)

To Live
——From Her Post Cards Sent to Noriko, with Her Poems Printed: Handy Made (1)

For corona, the self- restraint of going out
Was not the ban, though it was close to it.
Going out for taking foods and going to clinics or hospitals,
Were excepted for, they said.
Wearing masks, disinfection, washing hands and
Keeping two meters apart from next persons,
Which were to be strictly regulated.

Keeping these rules, as soon as possible,
We had to finish doing our things and come back home.
Gargling, washing from our finger tips to wrists with soap,
As deliberately as possible,
We had to resist against corona virus invisible.

I cannot walk, nor take something heavy.
But I had to eat something, so
Living within smallest areas for me to be permitted,
In so far as I could put up with.
Taking cares of accidents and tumbling down,
I thought I should live the tomorrow, looking only forwards.
It might have seemed stubborn for my old age.

Translator's Note: The poet sent me this card on postal mail,
which I received on July 9th.

(Translator: Noriko Mizusaki)

両手を上げる

今日は　どうして過ごそう
何をして時間を使おう
どんなことが楽しいか
ストレスなし　鬱なし
心躍るいいことはないか

メールを開く
ポストを見る
暫くぶりの手紙を書く
ちょっぴり散歩に出ようか
行く当てもなく幻の散歩

春秋長ず
ずいぶん歳を重ねたものだ
老いは若さを思い出すためにある
若き良き時代
恋と　活力と　体力
精一杯両手を上げてみる

＊訳者註：今回は市川ツタさんの作品はいつものように書き下ろしではなく、女史がいつも便箋入りのお手紙、あるいはお葉書として定期的にお送り下さる作品集の中から選抜、掲載をお願いした。（車椅子で）あまり活発とは言えない生活の中で、むしろ雄弁に市川さんは老いの日々を活用し、旺盛な創作実践と共に暮らしておられると思ったからでもある。

Raising My Hands Up

Today, how shall I spend?
What shall I use my hours for killing time?
How can I enjoy myself?
Without any stresses, and any depressions,
Can I do something just nice, dancing my heart?

Opening my mails out,
Checking my mailbox,
I wonder I shall write a letter after long?
Shall I happen to go out for a walk?
It is illusionary, because, with no destination.

Years so many passed to my elderly age,
I wonder how long a life I have spent.
The old age exists for us, to remind us of our young times;
Fresh and good days,
I spent with lovers, energy, and physical strength.
I am raising my hands up, as high as I can.

*Translator's Note: This time, in PANDORA, I asked Tsuta to publish her two poems, which was sent to me, on postal mail, In the form of postal cards. Using the wheel chair means, she is not so active for moving and going out, but, using the handicap, she shows us a surprising amount of poem makings, which tell us, so much the more eloquently, of the old and elderly days.

(Translator: Noriko Mizusaki)

山本由美子（日本・姫路）

扉

待つ人のいる扉
気配のない扉

笑い声のもれる扉
押し黙る扉

バタンと閉まる扉
カチリと響く扉

ふたりを分かつ扉
ふたりを守る扉

過去を遮る扉
夢を繋ぐ扉

Yumiko Yamamoto (Japan / Himeji)

Doors

A door with someone waiting
A door with no one inside

A door that spills laughter
A door that forces silence

A door that bangs
A door that clicks

A door that separates the two
A door that protects the two

A door that blocks our past
A door that leads to our dreams

(Translator: Yumiko Yamamoto)

言葉には限界がある

失ったとき
泣きたいとき

話さなくていい
伝えようとしなくていい

なにも言わないから
なにも聞かないから

こうして腕の中で
じっとしていればいい

Words Fall Short

When you feel the loss
When you feel like crying

You need not talk
Or explain anything

I will not say a word
Or ask for any

Just stay still
In my arms
Like this

(Translator: Yumiko Yamamoto)

前原正治（日本・宮城）

うみにしずむ
——鎮魂歌

いままでみにつけおぼえてきたものは
みなおぼえることのないおぼろなことばかり
ばらばらにふれたりみつめてきたものは
みなばらばらにとおくくずれるものばかり
いましおみずがしみこんでくると
もうわたしのものといえるものはなにもなく
しろいばらのはなびらのように
わたしのほねはゆるくそのみをひらき
あらゆるわたしはあわくあわのようにきえ
そしておもいだせないおもいでをおもいだすとき
おもわずなにものへでもないわらいがうかぶように
すべてがほのかにまるくまんげつのようにあらわれ
それからすべてがすべてを
ひろびろとひろげながらおもいだす
ねむるようにわすれるように

Shoji Maehara (Japan/ Miyagi)

Sinking Into The Sea
—Requiem

things I have put on and learned were
all those things vague and forgettable
things I have touched on and seen separately
were all that could fall in pieces far away
now the brine begins to infiltrate through
there remains nothing that I can claim as my own
like petals of a white rose
my bone opens its body slowly
all of me goes out in bubbles
when I recall something hard to remember
I smile in spite of myself at nothing especially
so the whole comes out faintly round like a full moon
then everything remembers it extending
everything far and wide
as if in a sleep or in forgetfulness

(Translator: Ruriko Suzuki)

梁瀬重雄（日本・埼玉）

農繁期

いつの間に　こんな歳になるまで
毎年農業をやって来てしまった

あわただしく
あの鼻どり　麦刈や稲の収穫
大豆や綿などあらゆる野菜の収穫
これらすべて手作業の記憶が
風化することなく
いまなお胸の奥深く染みついていて
時どき過激な農繁期の夢にうなされる

私はいつも子供の姿で手伝い
畑にはいつも父母　家族の姿が
座っては立ち　消えては現われ
強い陽射しに汗と涙に塗れ働いていた

＊鼻どり：田畑を耕す際、牛馬の鼻を取って誘導する役。

Shigeo Yanase (Japan/ Saitama)

On the Agricultural Season

Sometime before I get aware myself
Till at this elderly age of mine
I have been working for agriculture.
It was so busy the working
As taking a horse by grasping his nose into plowing fields*
Or working for the harvest of every kind of vegetables
Like soy beans and the cotton plants.
These memories of my working with hands
Have not faded away nor be gone from me
But keep staying thick at the depths of my bosom
Giving me nightmares on the agricultural season
That is excessively busy and hard.

In the nightmares I always helped them as a boy
In the fields there always my parents with my family members
Sitting and standing up: vanishing and appearing again and again
Smeared with sweat and tears on their faces they were working.
In the heated light of the sun.

(Ttanslator: Noriko Mizusaki)

*Translator's Note: "Taking a horse by grasping his nose into the plowing fields": the labor is called in brief, "taking by the nose" in Japanese.

正月　五

昨年は六月の長雨
八月の猛暑による高温障害で
農作物は経験した事にない大凶作だった

米が余る　暴落の時代
　　農業が滅び行く
貧困に苦しむ農民は
土を労わる事すらできない
時代は風のように通り過ぎて行き
百姓に救いの手を差しのべないだろう

しかしぼくは
農民の奉仕の姿
とめどなく流れる汗と涙と
米の味覚を忘れることはない

たとえ自然と共に生きる
農耕民族の姿が
今年も消えて行ったとしても

On a New Year's Day: (5)

Last year we had a long rain in June
The scorching heat in August gave us
Troubles caused by the high temperature.
Farm products had so worst a harvest
That I had never experienced before.

Rice prices slump down because of the over-product
  Now is the time when our agriculture would go dying?
Those who suffer poverty
Could not afford to take good cares of their soil
Time will go passing by like a wind
It will not stretch his helping hands to farmers

However I shall never forget
Farmers' serving labors for their harvests
Their sweats and tears running down with no ends
And the taste of the rice cooked for meals

Even if this year again should go decreased
The agricultural people who live together with nature.

(Translator: Noriko Mizusaki)

渡邊那智子（日本・東京）

ミルクティーの彼方

ミルクティーの彼方に浮かぶ
祖母の姿は痩せて哀しい

衰える光を追って
茂みの中に見つけた
僕達の素顔

砕け散り
蒼ざめる
水底は
一面のクローバー

夕陽が蜘蛛の巣にかかったよ！

遠く
遠く

秘蹟の町を
燕が過ぎる

（初出「詩霊」）

Nachiko Watanabe (Japan/ Tokyo)

BEYOND MILK TEA

Grandmother beyond milk tea
Looks thin and sorrowful

Chasing the fading light
We find in the bush
Our bare faces

Which break to pieces
And turn pale
At the bottom of water
Clovers overspread

Look! The setting sun is caught in the spider's web!

Far
Far away

A swallow flies
Through the city of sacrament

(Translator: Nachiko Watanabe)

短詩詩連

盗人（ぬすびと）

空よ
何を隠しているのか
そんなにも蒼ざめて

対岸

亡き父の夢を見た
野宿していたという

春雨

イシスの
涙

星屑

いまわの
猫が
置いていった

晴日

心に
雪が
降る

（初出「詩霊」,「時調」）

Short Poems

Stealer

Sky!
What do you conceal?
You look so pale

Opposite Shore

I saw my late father in a dream
He said he had slept in the open

Spring Rain

Tears
Isis shed

Stardust

Left
By a cat
On deathbed

Bright Day

Snow
Falls
In heart

(Translator: Nachiko Watanabe)

藤谷恵一郎（日本・大阪）

移ろい

風のように　移ろえ
時のように　移ろえ

風を櫂に
時を櫂に

空ろなれば
虚ろなれば
移ろいは明るさ

時よ　おまえは留まることを許さぬ
生き物の悲しみはおまえを貫き

風よ　おまえは人間の心を裸にし
留まることの汚れのような痛みを知らせる

命よ錨となるな
死よ錨となるな

命が舟であるならば
死よ白き帆であれ

Keiichiro Fujitani (Japan/ Osaka)

Changes

Go change like a wind
Go change like time

Turn the wind into an oar
Turn time into it, too

If it is empty
If it is nothing
Changing is up to light

Time! You do not permit us to stay
Sadness of all creatures penetrating you

Wind! You blow off human's hearts to be naked
Letting us know staying is a painful disgrace

Life! You do not turn into an ankor
Death! So you do neither

If life is a boat
Death! You be the white sail!

(Translator: Noriko Mizusaki)

秋葉信雄（日本・千葉）
Nobuo Akiba (Japan/ Chiba)

Paradise in jail

Do you remember what happened at Iwakuni ?
Yes I remember how I reached to Urumqi[1]
We used to know Iwakuni has the nice base
A coo1 girl from Urumqi sang and danced in that place

We went through the gate of Iwakuni by lying
Just only to have fun in Paradise to dying
So you said " 1 know your commander and I'm his friend
We're five from Taiwan, Malaysia, Hungary and Los in blend"

So many soldiers backing from Viet Nam were drinking there
You played the guitar and shouted rock'n'roll up flared
Hungarian couple stripped their clothes and danced on the stage
I pushed Urumqi girl to be naked and sing in the cage

Everybody called us " In 73 dope five"
Paradise in jail, the priority seat to drive

*Translator's Note 1: Iwaki and Urumqi. Iwaki is situated in Fukushima prefecture, in Japan. Urumqi, 烏魯木斉 is a large city in China, in the farthest west area, situated in Shinjang Uyghur Aptonom Rayoni.

The Secret Code

Before this station was built
The situation was killed
But you know the time was filled
And then the type was really milled

And then the road you're making
To the stars on you're taking
To the moon after faking
Everything in your mind shaking

Roll it over, scroll it closer
When you do it under controller
Wherever you go tell me no, sir
And you'll know who's the grocer

High away along the road
Get back to the secret code

(Mr. Akiba's original English poems)

植木信子（日本・新潟）

新緑の光に

切々と生きて
人たちのあいだに生きて
希望のように手を胸を足を叩いた
消しても痣に残る痕跡はわたしだけのものであっても
なぞり、埋もれる記憶から書き留めておく
あなたが忘れてしまっていても覚えておく
この世界にいたことを
いなくなった沢山の人たちの中でたった一人のあなたを
多くの人たちの悲しみの重さの中であなたの想いを
あなたは人々のあいだで笑い　話し　生きていた
背をまるめ三つ四つ顔を寄せあっていたときに
新緑の葉がゆれていて
木漏れ日が斑にさして葉陰をつくった
手を差しのべ手を握ったとき
あなたを流れる血が鼓動と重なってわたしにも流れた
その温もりを覚えておく
微笑み、あなたの口もとが動いて耳に伝わった言葉の振動を
沢山のとても沢山の人たちが生きられなくても
たった一人のあなたを胸におく
世界を覆う厚い黒雲の下でも
わたしたちは美しさを、幸せを変えたりはしないだろう
人たちの中にいて出逢い愛し生活し働き老いていくことの
新緑の薄緑に紅の桃の花や白ツツジの花が綺麗だ
広がる空の青や暮れなずむ日の長さ
夜明けの快い風

Nobuko Ueki (Japan/ Niigata)

For The light of Fresh Green Leaves

I have been living, as hard as I can,
Living among people,
Slapping my hand, chest, and feet, as if slapping hope.
Even if the scar marks that remained blue are only mine,
I shall write down, recalling them from my memories, half buried in the depths of my mind.
If you have lost the memory,
I shall not lose the memory that you once lived in this world,
I shall not forget only you, in so many people who passed away,
I shall not forget your memory, in spite of the thickest sadness for many people.
You were laughing among people, talking, and living your life.
When bending our backs round, we, gathering in three or four,
With our faces drawing closer,
The leaves of fresh green color were swaying,
And the sun rays coming through between trees in spots,
Throwing the leaves' shadows on the ground.
When I stretched my arms and grasped your hands,
Your blood circulated inside me, pushed by your heart pulses.
I shall never forget your warm hands,
Your smile, and your vibrations of your speeches I heard, when you moved your lips.
Even when so many people cannot live long,
I can put only you in my bosom.
Even under the thick dark clouds, which will cover all the world,
We shall not change our sense of beauty, nor the sense of happiness.

それから夏が来る
この世界の何かが変わっていっても
切々と生き抜く命を抱く地球
あなたの声を早くいってしまった人たちと聞く
(遠く　遠くになった……)
わたしは信じたい　人たちを
そこに喜びも憎しみもかけがえのない愛も暮らしがあることを
時が来て死んでいくことの不変さを
希望のように呼んでみる
あなたよ　逝ったあなたよ
それは約束のように緑の光に満ちている

We are living among people, meeting each other, loving, living, working, and
Getting old, which will be not changeable.
Fresh green leaves, red peach blossom, and white flowers of azaleas are beautiful.
The blue sky spreading above us, and long day till the dusky evening,
The pleasant wind at dawn is comfortable,
Then will come the summer.
If something of this world goes changing,
The earth will be holding lives, that try to live through, as hard as possible.
I hear your voice with the ones who passed away earlier than you.
(You gone far, far…)
I want to believe people, I want to believe,
That there are joy, hatred, and so precious love and with them we live.
It is not changeable that we have to die, when the time comes.
I would try to call you, like seeking for a hope. hope:
You! You, who passed way!
Death shall be filled with green light, just as a promise.

(Translator: Noriko Mizusaki)

8月1日の火　怒りの火

トノタン　トノタン　体のどこかで鳴っている
わけのわからない膨らむ悲しみが私を覆い
窓を抜けていく

梅雨明け近い夕暮れは茜が霞みに空にかかり
青い空の湖が茜を帯びている
雲はもっと茜色にかたまっている
川は水かさを増して岸辺の草をそよがせ
危うく撓う木の葉が微風に揺れている
もうすぐ日は暮れて　朝が来る

トノタン　トノタン
私の耳に鳴り続ける音は悲しみの音色
いっぱい死んだのだから
これからは生きていて下さい
三次元＋過去の時間と逝った人たちの時空に隙間があって
滑り込んだ人たちは行ったり来たりするという
神隠し　夢遊病者たちのこと　逝きそこねたもの
わけのないこの悲しみはその人たちの叫び
指笛の途切れる旋律がいっぱいに膨らんで
寂しいほとりに一人いる

夜明けに
ひどく憎く　ひどく愛しいと思ったのは誰にだろう
不動明王の炎の憤怒の形相は人の心のよう
阿修羅のたたかう心の模様　澄んだ瞳にこもれびが瞬く

私の体の隅に鼠の巣があってトノタントノタン囓る

Fire on August 1st; Fire of My Anger

Tono-tan, tono-tan, the sounds ring in some part of my body,
Some sadness I cannot know, swelling and covering me.
Goes out through my window.

In the evening, when soon a rainy season is ending,
The sky is tinted in orange color, misty,
As if a blue lake in the sky were painted in the color.
The clouds gather more congested in the color.
A river swelling gives the grass sways on the banks.
It blows blades on the riverside, almost bent down.
Soon it becomes dark and then a morning will come.

Tono- tan- tono- tan,
The sounds ring to my ears, in a sad tone of death.
So many people had passed away.
You should survive, at least, I request.
They say, because there is a space between the three dimensional past time and the time for the dead,
The ones who happened to slide into it will come and go, crossing the border:
Such ones as the hidden ones by gods, sleepwalkers and the ones half dead.
The vague sadness with no definite reason is their cries.
The breaking melody of someone's fingers' whistling swells full in the air,
I am standing alone, on the lonesome shore.

At dawn,
To whom did I feel hateful and so dear?
The facial expression of Fudo-Myoo King, a god of flaming fury, is just like our minds.

雨だれのように　病原のように広がって私を超えていく
だから　あなたを探したりしない
超えられない罪の痛みには黙って寄りかかるだけ
蝋燭のように指が燃えたとて美しいひと、
かぐわしい香　俤だけの
トノタン　トノタン　悲しみの襞の甘さに潜むのなら

ある片田舎の離れた家で
少年と少女はミルク入り紅茶とビスケットを食べたあと
流れ弾にあたったとの黄みがかる新聞の端に1、2行

8月1日　夜　怒りの火は一晩街を燃え尽くしていた

＊訳者註1：仏教では不動明王は憤怒の形相の神であり、（阿）修羅は戦闘の神である。守護神ともみなされる。

＊訳者註2：本詩は1945年8月1日の午前10時30分から翌日8月2日の午前0時10分まで続いた、米軍による長岡、新潟空襲に言及している。

Ashura[1], a gurdian god, who has patterns for fighting in his mind.
In his clear eyes, twinkling the sunray, coming down through branches.

I have a nest of rats in some corner of my body.
They have a biting sound as tono-tan, tono-tan.
Like rain drops, and like germs, they go spreading beyond me.
So, I shall not search for you,
In silence, I lean against my pain of guilty which cannot be ended.
You were beautiful, even if like a candle, your fingers were burned out,
Your fragrance I sense, just only in my memory.
I chant as Tono-tan, tono-tan, if we have to lurk in the sweetness of sorrowful pleats.

In a remote house from a city,
After a boy and a girl had milk tea and cookies.
They were hit by stray bullets, and killed.
That was reported in one or two lines on a newspaper in the corner.
It has turned yellowish yet.

On August 1st, at night, the fires were burning the town out, all night long[2].

*Translator's Note 1: Fudo Myo King and Ashura are Buddhist gods for fires and fury.

*Translator's Note 2: This poem refers to the air-raids over Nagaoka, Niigata, attacked by the US air forces. They continued from August 1st, 10:30 a.m. to August 2nd, 0:10 a.m. in 1945.

(Translator: Noriko Mizusaki)

松尾静明（日本・広島）

夾竹桃の花が

夾竹桃の　白い花が　咲いている
ことしも　いっぱいに　咲いている
あの日　夢と　未来を　焼かれた少女の
清らかに白く　強い祈りのように
　ふたたび　こころを　こわさないで
　ふたたび　からだを　くずさないで

夾竹桃の　紅い花が　咲いている
ことしも　いっぱいに　咲いている
あの日　希望と　明日を　くだかれた少年の
静かに紅く　強い願いのように
　ふたたび　子どもたちを　連れ去らないで
　ふたたび　ちちやははを　うばわないで

この世界が
花のこころで
愛のこころで
歌のこころで
満ちあふれますように

ことしも　いっぱいに　咲いている
ことしも　いっぱいに　叫んでいる

Seimei Matsuo (Japan/ Hiroshima)

Bamboo Peaches Blossom

White blossoms of bamboo peaches are in bloom,
This year again, they flower out now in full,
They are pure- white and strong, like a girl's prayer.
Her dream and future were burned away on the day.
  Do not break down our hearts again,
  Do not destroy our bodies again.

Red blossoms of bamboo peaches are in bloom,
This year again, they flower out now in full.
They are calmly blooming out strong, just like a boy's wish.
His hope and tomorrows were destroyed on the day.
  Do not take away our children again,
  Do not deprive us of our parents again.

May this world be fill out
With the hearts like the blossoms,
With the hearts of love,
With the hearts of songs.

They are blooming out in full,
They are protesting out in full.

(Translator: Noriko Mizusaki)

（こどもかけあいうた）
大橋　小橋

おおはし　こはし
どちらを　わたる

おおはしの　むこうに
わたると　なにがある

なんにもない
あかいはなが　たおれてる

こはしの　むこうに
わたると　なにがある

なんにもない
あおいはなが　たおれてる

おおはし　わたらん
こはし　わたらん

おおはし　わたれ
あかいはな　くれてやる

おおはし　わたらん

こはし　わたれ
あおいはな　くれてやる

こはし　わたらん　　　　（くりかえす）

(A Children's Song for Dialogue)
Big Bridge and Small Bridge

A big bridge and a small bridge
Which shall I go across?

Crossing the Big One
What is there at the end?

Nothing is there
A red flower fallen down

Crossing the Small One
What is there at the end ?

Nothing is there
A blue flower fallen down

Let's cross the Big Bridge
Let's cross the Small Bridge

Cross the Big Bridge
I'll give you red flowers

Let's cross the Big Bridge

Cross the Small Bridge
I'll give you blue flowers

Let's cross the Small Bridge (repeat)

(Translator: Noriko Mizusaki)

志田静枝（日本・長崎・大阪交野）

月と　丸ボウロ

スーパームーンに会いたくて
月明りを浴びながら　期待しつつ
丸ボウロを手に夜空を見上げた
新聞では二月十九日か二十日が
月の見頃だと書いていたけれど
一日遅れてしまった二十一日の夜は
月も星の欠片も見えない

残念だったけれど
丸ボウロをかじるしかなかった
優しい味だ　故郷長崎の丸ボウロは
微(かす)かな潮騒の気配を感じさせる
その味につい甘えたくて
また一枚食べたくなる　また一枚　もう
月なんか忘れて　どうでもよくて
次から次へと食べている私

二〇一九年二月二十一日の宵と闇との
狭間の風は冷気を運んでくる

Shizue Shida (Japan/ Nagasaki/ Osaka)

The Moon and My Nagasaki Sweets

I wanted to see the full moon.
In the moon light, with the expectation,
I looked up in the sky, with round cakes in my hand.
The newspaper said that on February 19th or 20th
Would be best for the moon watching, but
On the night of the 21th, one day delayed,
I could not see any of the moon nor even a shard of a star.

It was a pity for me,
I had nothing but the round cake. It tasted sweet.
That was a special product of Nagasaki, my birth place.
It reminded me of faint sounds of sea waves.
Indulged in the sweetness, with no help to me,
I liked to bite one more of it, and the next one, then,
Having forgotten the moon, no more on it,
I was eating them, one after the next.

On February 21th, 2019, the wind carried me the chilly air,
At the time between the evening and the darkness.

(Translator: Noriko Mizusaki)

韓国の茶葉

海を越えて隣国の若い友から
心を込めて選んでくれたお味は
爽やかなキムさん　あなたの香りを忍ばせ
小さな湯飲み茶わんの中に揺れる面影
手元で花開く茶葉の緑から
心通わす露の玉が転がり出る

微かな渋みは木槿(むくげ)の花の余情を思い
かげろう私の真意と　重なり合う調べに
木槿の花は好きよ　そっとつぶやく
複雑な香りはしばし私を隣国へいざなう
微かな甘みは　かつて韓国の地で味わった
山苺ワインの甘さと含羞が
キムさん　あなたと重なるわ

初の私のエッセイ集「渚に寄せる波」
の返礼に　若いキムさんは
茶葉を選んで贈ってくれた
韓国の風と　あなたにも会いたいな
何時かその日が来ることを願いつつ
その日が何時か　今私にもわからない

Tea Leaves from Korea

Sent from my young friend in the next country, over the sea,
A gift of green tea, which you selected for your gift to me.
The taste reminds me of your fragrance, dear Ms.Kim,
I see your image sway in my small tea cup.
Out of the green color, like blooming in my hands,
The dew drops come rolling out, which will link you and me.

The bit astringency reminded me of a rose of Sharon,
It like a music, overlapping with my loving heart to you,
"I love a rose of Sharon," whispered I to myself.
The delicate fragrance, for some time would likely invite me to your country,
The delicate sweet wine of the mountain strawberrries,
I am now thinking of,
Which I once tasted in Korea.
It had a faint sweet flavor, as if it were shy.
Which overlaps with your memory, Ms. Kim!

For her return gratitude to my first book,
My collected essays, *WAVES ON THE BEACH*,
Ms. Kim, presented the Korean tea with sweets, to me.
She selected it. She is a young lady.
I am now dreaming of the Korean wind and you, Ms. Kim,
Wising that the day will come upon me, sometime.
Though, when is the day, now even I cannot know, myself.

(Translator: Noriko Mizusaki)

新谷頼子（日本・大阪）
Yoriko Niiya (Japan/ Osaka)

ペルシアへの旅
Travelling to Persia

バラの花咲く頃、エスファハンは最高に美しい
The season of Rose's flower
Isfahan is the most beautiful in Iran

青いタイルの丸い屋根、シェイクロトファッラモスクと言って、シャーアッバース王の命令によって王家のために建てられたもの
Mosque Sheykh Lotf –olallah was built by Shah Abbas the Great at 17 C.

それはまるではちの巣のようで、とても細かいデザインのイスラム建築。
It is like a blue beehive, very small fine, delicate of design of Islamic building.

広い広場にはバザールがあり、さばくの甘いお菓子、ミニアチュールの絵、ペルシアサラサの店があった。
I went to the big huge an open space, there were many kinds of shops, in bazaar, sweets of Gaz (dessert), miniature of Persian historical picture, and Persian Chints (sarasa) printed cotton.

教会に入り、美しいキリストの生涯の絵を見た。
I went to the Vank Church, found out beautiful picture of life of Christ.

メナールジョンバンと言って、14世紀の揺れる聖塔があった。
Menar Jonban is called, the shaking holy tower of 14 C.

エスファハンから古い村落のヤズトへ車で行って、
From Isfahan to the old village Yazd, I moved by car.

途中さばくを通って、
On my way, through the desert place,

最古のゾロアスタ教徒が住んでいる所に着いた。
I arrived at the oldest village of Zoroastrians.

マルコ・ポーロも13世紀にヨーロッパ人はじめて訪れたそうだ。
I heard that Marco Polo, Italian traveler who visited here in 13 C, as the first visitor of Europeans.

ここは繊維産業が有名な所
Here is famous for textile industry in Iran.

丘のふもとに泉があり、
On the foot of the hill, there was the spring, gushing out pure and clean, fresh water.

両手ですぐにすくいあげ、飲んでみた
Soon I tried to scoop and drink with my hands.

とってもおいしかった。
Oh Good! It tasted very good.

私のかわいたのどをうるおしてくれた
I feel to be moistened with my dry throat. It made me fresh and charm.

どこからか吹いてくる心地よい風を頬に受け、
The wind is blowing from somewhere, I accept comfortable, soft, gentle breeze with my cheeks.

心は何か満足を感じ、神秘な神の声をききましょう。
I know and find contentment. Let's listen to the mysterious God's voice now,

感謝　心で祈った。
I pray to God with mind of gratitude.

感謝をこめて
With my gratitude.

(Translator: Yoriko Niiya)

ペルシアのことわざ1　　ペルシアのことわざ2

Persian Proverbs

志田道子（日本・東京）

気分はいいさ

コロナと生きる？
ああ、まったく
こんなことが起きるとは思ってもみなかった
こんなに長い間
みんなが家に閉じ込められて
“あたしは人づきあいが嫌い”
“ひとりで居るのがいい”
そんな主義は吹っ飛んだ
毎日毎日積み重なった緊張で
疲れたよ
人生に？　ひとに？　歴史に？
運命よ　あなたにだ
あなたはわたしに恥ずべき人間としての命を与えた
この地球上に生きる全てを公平には扱わず
自分の都合にだけ合わせようとする人間
過度な野心、過度な競争、過度なお祭り騒ぎで
地球の存亡を危機に陥れた人間
いま、自然はわたしたちにコロナという薬を撒いたのかも知れない
地球が受けている苦痛を終わらせるため
人間の過度な盲目的な欲望を終わらせるため
（まるで猛り狂うウイルスのような）わたしたちを
コロナという別のウイルスで消毒するため！
……たぶん、……でも
わたしの気分はいいさ
この心地よく晴れた夏の朝
いつものとおりコーヒーを一杯テーブルの上に置いて

Michiko Shida (Japan/ Tokyo)

I feel fine though

With Corona?
Oh, Yah,
No one waited such a spectacle in life
Never thought forced to cage in home
So long time
“I don’t like social intercourse”
“I prefer solitude”
All policy dispersed with emotional exhaustion
Which accumulated day by day
I am tired
With life? With people?   With history?
With you, Destiny
You’ve born me as a shamed human
Who see only its convenience but treating fairly all being on our planet Earth
Who is making a risk of the earth’s termination by its ;
Too much ambition, too much rivalry, too much horseplay
Now the nature might give us a dose of his own medicine, Corona
To terminate its pain
To terminate human being’s excessive sightless desire
To disinfect us (being like a rampage virus) by another virus, Corona!
…Perhaps…,   but
I feel fine though, by my cup of coffee on the table as usual
On this lovely sunny morning

*Recited in Tokyo Poetry Reading 2020 in the Zoom Congress

(Translator: Michiko Shida)

酒井力（日本・佐久）

空の道

不意にいま
街角を曲がって
彼方へ消えて行った托鉢姿は
あれは誰の似姿だったのだろう

想いはいつも決まって
旅へと駆り立てられる
が
どこへも行くまい
何かが見えてくるまで
何かをはっきりさせるまで

弓道試練を毎朝続けるのは
ひとつには
自分を捨てるため
とはいっても
心を空にすることではない
様々な欲心を去って
ひたすら磨く

心を開き
「会者定離（えしゃじょうり）」の理に
心身をゆだねる
禅の修行のため道を行く托鉢僧
前向きに生きようとすることの

Tsutomu Sakai (Japan/ Saku)

A Way to the Empty-Minded
(Engaged in a Japanese Martial Art)

Suddenly just now,
I saw a mendicant priest turn at the corner,
Then he disappeared from my sight.
Whose figure did he resemble?

I am always thinking of going travel.
But,
I shall not go out,
Till I can see something essential to me,
Till I can make something valued clear out.

I practice the Japanese archery exercise every morning.
One reason is,
For getting rid of my worldly self.
Though I say so,
It is not to make my mind void, but,
Myself to be delivered from various worldly desires.
For which I only try to improve myself.

Opening my mind,
I commit myself to the principle as follows:
"Sooner we meet, than we are destined to part form each other."
The mendicant priest travelling for his Zen training,
I saw in him the one who tries to have a positive life for himself,

確認の日々
捨てることから生まれた
ひとすじの道
積乱雲のかがやき

His days for the assurance.
From leaving worldly self,
A way was born
The cumulonimbus clouds shine bright,
In the sky.

(Translator: Noriko Mizusaki)

黒い蝶
——いのち寂（しず）む日のために

山法師の白い花影に
川は
死せるものたちの
まなざしを映し
はこんでいる

水は絶えることなく
わたしのなかに
流れこみ
それはいつ消えるのか
だれも知らない

父と母と
それに兄たちも
この川に生まれ
せせらぎを聴いて育ち
そして
いつの日か
旅立っていったが……

やさしかった心根は
ひらひら揺れ
黒い背に寂（しず）もり
なつかしい声になって
ひびいてくる

川面を舞う

Black Butterfly
——For the Day of Nirvana

In the shadows of white flowers
Of the Japanese Dogwoods,
The river is
Reflecting the eyes of the dead
Carrying them.

The water without any stops,
Come flowing
Into me,
When it disappears
Nobody knows.

My parents,
And brothers were,
Born to this river.
They grew up listening to the stream.
Then, some day,
They passed away.

Their hearts were so tender.
They sway fluttering,
On the black back they gathered lonely,.
Then transforming into nostalgic voices,
They come on echoing.

Fluttering on the surface of the water,
You a butterfly!

一羽の蝶よ
おまえはいつから
そこを棲かとしているのだろう

雨風に抗い
源流めざしてさかのぼる
無の連鎖
永遠いのちへと続く
一筋の
小さな光よ

Since when
You are dwelling there?

Resisting weathers
Going up the river aiming at the source,
It is the links of nothingness
Led to the eternal life,
A shaft of
Smallest light.

(Translator: Noriko Mizusaki)

永井ますみ（日本・神戸）

七夕歌

吾がまだ若くて朝廷へ出仕していなかった頃の話だ
吾が家の庭に筵を延べ燈明を灯し
ひとり七夕歌を作ったことがあった六十首もだ
筆を執り筆を置き
神憑りのようであったと今さらに懐かしい
東の空に星を箒で掃き散らしたような天の川が輝きを増してくる
その星々をかき分けかき泳ぎ
彦星になりかわり
織姫になりかわり歌う

年にありて今か枕くらむ　ぬばたまの夜露隠りに遠妻の手を *[1]

天の川に細い月を浮かべてみたりもした
遠い唐の七夕の話では女が男を訪なうというが
吾が国には男が訪れる妻問いの習いがある
女からの誘いの使いをもんもんとして待っている吾らが習い
いっそ今から訪なうべきか

秋風の清き夕べに天の川　船こぎ渡る月人男 *[2]

＊1　2035番 一年に一度の今夜、遠妻の手をまき寝るか夜霧がくれに
＊2　2043番　秋風のすがしい夕べ、天の川を漕いで渡るよ月人男は

Masumi Nagai (Japan/ Kobe)

Songs for a Star Festival

It was at the time when I was young and did not go to work at the court.
I spread a straw mat in my yard and burning oil to light it up,
Sitting on it I made songs for the star festival alone, as many as sixty works.
I took up a blush pen and put it down,
It was as if I was haunted by gods, which even now I remember it so nostalgic.
In the east sky, the heavenly river was getting brighter and brighter,
It was just like stars were scattered, swept with a broom.
Parting them apart with my hands and swimming among them.
I sang songs for the sake of Altar, the male star,
For Vega, the princess weaver.

Now shall I go meet with my wife, who is parted by the river,
Hiding myself behind night dews dark, cross it for her hand.[*1]

I tried to float a thin moon on the water of the heavenly river,
In the legend of the Tang dynasty, far, I hear a woman visited a man,
In our land we have a practice that a man would visit a woman.
We are patiently waiting for a messenger coming from the woman.
So from now I shall visit her myself.

The autumn wind clear in the evening, a man of the moon,
Shall g across the heavenly river, rowing a boat to his wife. [*2]

*Note 1, 2: They are the songs of Yakamochi Otomo, quoted from *The Thousands of Collected Poems*, the most ancient poetry anthology of Japan.

佐々木洋一（日本・宮城）

キミ

「目のキツイ女が好きだ」
キミはそう言い残すと　夕暮れの道を去って行った
へいわな別れとはこんなことをいう
曲がりくねった道でなく真っ直ぐなどこまでも真っ
直ぐな道

しっぽを置いて行った
振り向くことが上手なはずなのに
振り向かなかった

ふさふさのしっぽの感触が今でも残っている
置いて行ったものがほのかに温（ぬく）い
ほのかに匂う　ほのかにたたずむ

「目のキツイ女が好きだ」
ボクがそう思うのはキミの影響だ
しっぽの後を憑いて行きたい
しっぽの先をくすぐりたい

土手のところで叫んでみた
こーん　こーん
キミは戻って来ない

ずいぶんたったはずなのに
稲荷の前を通るときまって思い出す

Yoichi Sasaki (Japan/ Miyagi)

YOU

"You like a woman with sharp eyes."
Leaving the speech to me, you went walking away
on the road in the evening.
A peaceful parting is supposed to be such one.
It is not winding road, but straight, endlessly
Straight a road.

You left your tail behind.
You should have been good at looking back,
But you did not look back.

The touch of your furry tail is still vivid.
The thing you left behind is faintly warm,
Faintly fragrant: faintly standing up still.

"I like a woman with sharp eyes."
My thinking so is influenced by you.
I want to follow your tail, charmed.
I want to tickle the tip.

I try to give a loud cry on a bank,
" Come on! Come on! Why not? "
You never come back[1].

Though it passed so many years since then,

キミが置いていったしっぽのへいわなしぐさ

暗闇に紛れたしっぽがやみくもに踊り出す
「目のキツイ女が好きだ」
夜通し曲輪の内で踊っている

When I go past the fox shrine[2], I remember
The peaceful movements of the tail you left behind.

In darkness, suddenly it starts dancing around.
"You like a woman with sharp eyes."
It does not stop dancing all night in a yard of the shrine.

*Translator's Note 1: In Japanese, foxes cry, as "con, con," which means, also, "has not come" in Japanese. Yoichi's original Japanese version has these double meanings, with his crying. It cannot hardly be put into English.

*Translator's Note 2: The Inari shrine is a shrine for worshipping a god of harvests, especially, the rice harvest, as well as a god of arts and performances like music, dances and singing songs. In a folk faith, the god turned into a fox god. In Japan, performers or artists are expected to visit the shrine, praying for their prosperity.

(Translator: Noriko Mizusaki)

プリーティ・セングプタ（インド・ニューヨーク）
Preety Sengupta (India/ New York)

Haiku on Corona

コロナ俳句

(1) Name so feminine
Behaviour demonic
Mocking assassin

あざ笑う
名は女性的
殺人鬼

(2) Beware of us all
Our claps, bells, cymbals and Om
Saying “Be Thou Gone”

気を付けろ
鉦や太鼓は
死ね！の意味

(3) Stay away? Apart?
Should not be near? Not hug?
Yes, ready; I am not scared.

距離保て？
抱き合うなかれ？
冗談じゃない

(4) Isolating me
Shall not kill me, nor my love
For the World, for Life.

隔離でも
あたし死なない
死ぬものか

(5) Tulips? Daffodils?
Lament, O traveller’s heart -
Deprived of Beauty

花は何処？
嘆け　旅人
コロナ剥奪

(6) Silent tears serge,
All strangers are family.
Helpless empathy.

涙しとど
にんげん家族
えにし分断

（日本語訳：水崎野里子）

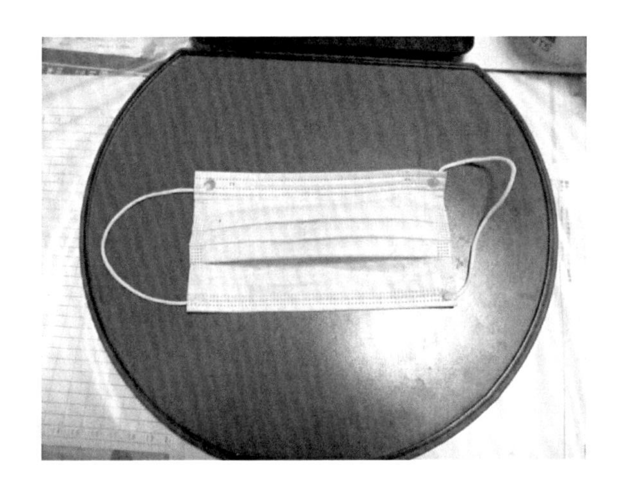

安森ソノ子（日本・京都）

オックスフオードへ

パリを経てロンドンに滞在
私は一人オックスフォードまでの電車に揺られていた
向かい合わせのシートの間に
小さな机がある

車内でノートを広げられる
苦労もなく文字も書ける
郊外の線路は国土の香をふくみ
自ずと先人の詩が胸に住む

1788年に生まれたショージ・ゴードン・パイロンの声　脊を動かし
あの詩編「シヨンについてのソネット」の冒頭が広がっていく
“自由よ！　鉄鎖に抗する精神を守る、永遠の霊よ！
お前は牢獄にあってこそ真の生彩を発揮する”

1816年にスイスのシヨン城を訪れたパイロンは記した
シヨン城の牢獄に幽閉されたジュネーブの人・ボンニバードに
政治的自由と宗教の改革を呼んだ魂に
パイロンは　ほとばしる想いを捧げた

人道的な強い心音は　近づく学徒の多い街へ誘い　語る
自由を考えさす道のりで

オックスフォードへの列車内は
動く書斎の　限りある貴重な時間

（『紫式部の肩に触れ』安藤ソノ子英日詩集より）

Sonoko Yasumori (Japan/ Kyoto)

Toward Oxford

After Paris and London I'm on my way to Oxford.
I am rocked from side to side in a train bound for Oxford alone
I find a small table facing the opposite seat
I can open my notebook on it
And I can also write letters without difficulty.
The ourside green of the suburbs sends fragrance of the country to us.
A poem flashes suddenly.

I hear Lord Byron's voice: he was born in 1788
When I straighten myself up in my seat.
The voice sounds sonorously: "Eternal Spirit of the chainless Mind!
Brightest in dungeons, Liberty! Thou art;——
For there thy habitation is the heart——
The heart which love of thee alone can bind"

Lord Byron visited the Chillon Castle in Switzerland in 1816.
He sang of Bonnyvard, the Genevan reformist
The spirit who cried for political liberty and religious reform.
Byron dedicated his surging passion to his memory.

A strong humanitarian thought invites me toward the academic town
Full of students. Deeply I think of liberty in the train.

The moving train for me is my study where I can think——
The limited time, yet so precious.

*From A Bilingual Poetry Book by Sonoko Yasumori: *TOUCHING MURASAKI SHIKIBU'S SHOULDER*

(Translator: Sonoko Yasumori)

スイスからパリ大学へ

一人でパリへ向かった
1987年5月
インタビューの約束をかかえ
パリ大学へ直行
スイスでの国際ペンの大会後
パリ大学で政治学を専攻している青年と
にこやかに対話していた

澄んだ瞳のフランス人の若者は　話を続ける
「世界はどのように変わるのか　歩むのか
将来　東洋を訪れ　日本にも行ってみたい
今専攻している政治学に取り組む予定」
「私も日本で法学部政治学科で学んでいました
共通の話題は山ほどありそうですね」
住む国は異なっていても　志は分かりあい

2015年　父親はフランス人　母親は日本人である若者が
入学したパリ大学で
母のふるさと日本の京都を思う
彼は私の姉の娘の息子

僕の半分の血は日本
ママンの母国日本
東洋からの風のそよぎから
聞える　切なる願いが

「幼い頃　一緒に過ごした　姪のサト子ちゃん
あなたは　フランス人の博士と結婚して

From Switzerland to the University of Paris

I headed for Paris alone in May 1987
After the international competition in Switzerland
Because of the appointment to interview
I went directly to the University of Paris to talk cheerfully with a young man specializing in political science

The young French man with bright eyes kept talking
“How will the world change
How will it go
I would like to go to Japan in the Orient and like to do research in my specilalty in the future”
“I myself used to study politics at the faculty of law in Japan and have a lot to talk about in common”
Though our homelands are different, we have same aspirations

In 2015, a young man whose father is French and mother from Japan,
He thinks for his mother’s hometown, Kyoto in Japan at University of Paris which he entered
He is my elder sister’s grandson

Half of my blood is Japanese
My mother’s homeland is Japan
A breeze from the orient has sprung up
And I hear the sound of desire

“My niece Satoko
We used to spend together when we were young
You married a French doctor and became a French lady

フランス人になった
そう　あなたが選んだ人生で
今迄通り　しっかりと歩んで下さい
フランスの空のもと　縁ある人々を大切にして　充実した生涯でありますように
日本を　日本人のあなたを愛するサト子ちゃんの夫に　パリ大学に学ぶ息子に
親しみと敬意を抱いて　京都の旧家を守り　過ごしています」
サト子の母の妹より

Well, it's your life you have chosen
Just go with firm steps under French skies

May you live a full life
Think much of those near you
To your husband, who loves you as Japanese
And to her son, who studies at the University of Paris
I maintain our old family in Kyoto"
From your aunt

(Translator: Sonoko Yasumori)

山口敦子（日本・東京）

牧水挽歌

酔えば　酔う程（ほど）　辛くなる
父母（ちちはは）　済まぬと　詫びる夜半（よわ）
田代（たしろ）の　山々　日向灘（ひゅうがなだ）
思い出　深き　故郷（ふるさと）へ
錦（にしき）を　飾れる　日はいつか

ままに　ならない　恋ゆえに
悩みを　抱（いだ）いて　枯野行く
幾山河（いくやまかわ）　越え行く　故郷（ふるさと）の
坪谷（つぼや）の　里の　山桜
我が短歌（うた）　賛歌で　咲かせたい

「幾山河（いくやまかわ）　越えさり行かば　寂しさの
　　終（は）てなむ国ぞ　今日も旅ゆく」

友や　良い師に　出逢いつつ
白鳥（しらとり）　羽ばたく　海山（うみやま）の
自然に　抱（いだ）かれ　千本の
松原（まつばら）　守りて　晴れて今
歌人（うたびと）　牧水（ぼくすい）　ここに有り

作詞：山口敦子
作曲：美波有
編曲：大場吉信
唄：水木大介

Atsuko Yamaguchi (Japan/ Tokyo)

Elegy for Bokusui

The more intoxicated, the more painful, I turn,
Sorry for my parents! I apologize in a midnight,
The mountains in Tashiro and Hyuga-nada sea,
To my homeland full of my memories deep I miss,
When can I come back, as a right man in praise?

Because of my broken heart, my love forlorn,
Worries holding I go travelling on desolate fileds.
I am wandering across many mountains and rivers,
In Tsuboya, in my hometown, wild cherries!
I wish them to bloom out by my song in praise.

"How many mountains and rivers I should
 Go across, to the land which loneliness will end in?
  I go traveling out seeking for it, today, again"*

Meeting with best friends and best teachers,
Over seas, mountains a white bird goes flying,
Held by nature, guarded by thousands pine yards,
Now at last, a tanka poet Bokusui, here I stands.

*Translator's Note: The quotation of an original Bokusui's tanka song, the famous one.

Words: Atsuko Yamaguchi
Music: Yu Minami
Arrangement: Yoshinobu Oba
Song: Daisuke Mizuki

(Translator: Noriko Mizusaki)

市原礼子（日本・大阪）

皇帝ダリア

ああ　すてき
りゆうも　なく
だれからも　見られるって
いい　きもち
てんの　かぜに　ふかれて
うーんと　たかい　ところで
こうてい　ダリア

＊頭韻…後ろからこうていだりあ

Reiko Ichihara (Japan/ Osaka)

Emperor Dahlia

So nice a feeling! Ah!
With no special reasons
Watched by any persons
I am feeling so pleasantly
Blown by winds heavenly
I am Emperor dahlia in the sky
Bloom out at a position so high

*In couplets: rhyming every two lines at the ends.

(Translator: Noriko Mizusaki)

千日紅

千年の時を生きる？
いいえ　千日のあいだ咲き続ける
紅い花のさんざめき
のぞみ　やすこ　じゅんこ
はるみ　めぐみ　はつえ
何をささやいているの？
逝ってしまった笑みが風に揺れている

Globe Amaranth

Do they live for a thousand years?
No. They bloom out for a thousand days.
They enjoy making merry, together in chorus:
Globes of flowers for love.
Nozomi, Yasuko, Junko,
Harumi, Megumi and Hatsue,
What are you whispering?
Smiles gone from you sometime,
Now swing in the winds.

(Translator: Noriko Mizusaki)

安達原（あだちがはら）

安達原　鬼女の物語
舞台の周り　蝋燭が灯される
笛　鼓　太鼓が奏でられ
地謡が始まる

襲いかかる白頭の鬼女
山伏たちは数珠を揉んで祈る
追いつめられた鬼女が
どうしたことか童女に見えてきた

生き別れた娘とは知らず
身重の女を殺してしまい
そうと知って狂った女の末路が
私のなかで鳴り響く

骨壺を膝に抱いて斎場からの帰り道
眠気に骨壺を落としそうになった
こんなときにも眠くなるのだ
子を亡くしたのに

鬼になれなかったたくさんの私が
鬼女となって山伏と闘う
鬼女が祈り伏せられる
鬼女の哀しみを祈り伏せることはできない

鬼女の哀しみは消え去らない
哀しみが鳴り響いてやまない

ADACHUGAHARA: On the Noh Performance

ADACHIGAHARA* is a story of one ogress.
Around the stage candles were lighted,
The pipes and drums were played at the beginning,
Then started the chorus singing.

The ogress with gray hair tried to assault on the monks,
While they prayed for her, rubbing the beads of their rosaries.
Somehow I do not know, but she looked like a young girl,
Accused by them so severely.

Not knowing a young woman was her own daughter who she parted from her, alive,
She killed her. she was pregnant.
When she realized it, she was driven mad.
Her fate resounding inside me.

On the way back from the funeral place, holding her cremation urn on her laps,
Feeling sleepy, she was about to drop it.
I wondered at her sleepiness at such a time.
When she lost her daughter.

So many spirits of mine, that could not become an ogress,
Now becoming an ogress and fight against monks.
I am purged and purified of my crimes,
Yet they cannot pray down to calm my sadness.

Her sadness will never vanish.
It will not stop ringing out for ever.

(Translator: Noriko Mizusaki)

秋田高敏（日本・千葉）

今日があるでしょう

一日一日を無事に過せればそれでいいのです
欲はあるけれど
いつも裏切られてばかりいるから
もう欲深い夢は見ないことにしました

草花にたわむれる蝶のように
そよ風にゆられる柳のように
私の心も一日の中に溶けこみ
酸素を思い切り頂戴し
粗末な三度の食事に
舌鼓打てれば恩の字ですと

電車の隣席に座った
一期一会になるであろう高齢の婦人
話しかけているのか一人言なのか
どちらでもいい
話に頷きながら聞きいった

知らない間に誕生し
種々雑多な生きざまを経験して来たであろう
頬こけた唇には薄紅色がほどこされ
本人は苦笑のつもりかも知れないが
微笑みとして座席からこぼれ咲いてくる

もう子供達も孫達も遠くに住み

Takatoshi Akita (Japan/ Chiba)

I HAVE TODAY

I am satisfied if I can spend every day with safety
I have wishes but
Always I was betrayed
So now I shall have no more dreams ambitious

Just like a butterfly playing with flowers
Just like a willow swayed by a breeze
If I could melt myself into a day
Given a lot of oxygen as much as like
And I could relish my every poor meal
I shall be grateful

It was a tale of an old lady
She happened to sit next to me in a train
Whether she was speaking to me or
She muttered to herself
I do not mind at all
I nodded at her listening to her

Born before she got aware
She might have had various kinds of experiences in her life
On her lips below the bony cheeks pink lip stick put on
She might think it as a wry smile but
As a smile it comes bloom over from her seat

私は一人なのです
でも幸せなのです
一か月十万円にも満たない生活ですが
このように生きているということは
明日があるでしょう
明日ぽっくり死んでも
今日はこのように生きているでしょう

続けられるであろうこんな話を
いつまでも聞きたかったけど
そんな時間はない
次の駅で下車するしかない
窓越しに茜雲が返してくれる金の糸が
老婦人の頬の皴に一筋二筋と煌めき漂い
笑顔がこっくりと頷いてくれた

Now my children and grandchildren live far from me
I live alone
I am happy though
My living expenses is less than ten thousand yen a month but
That I can live in this way
Because I have tomorrow
If tomorrow I happened to die but
You see I live today in this way

Her tale might go on in so far as she would like it
I wanted to listen to her more but
I had no time then
I had to get off the train at the nest station
The orange red clouds bounded back golden threads
Through the window twinkling bright in a few shafts
Around the winkles on her cheeks
She gave me a happy smile nodding at me

(Translator: Noriko Mizusaki)

エドワード・レビンソン（日本・千葉・USA）

『ぼくの植え方』岩波書店刊より

春は先へ先へと進んでいき、ぼくは、山の中で自生する藤の花の写真撮影に、近くの谷へ車を走らせる。道路がとても狭いので、トラックを道路際に寄せて止める。そして一枚のショットを探して歩く。と、奇妙にも、背の高い草の後ろからラジオが聞こえてくるではないか。おばあさんが野菜畑で働いていて、ラジオはおばあさんと一緒にいてあげているのだ。ぼくが手を振ると彼女も振り返す。そこで高い草と蛇のいる可能性をものともせずに、彼女のところへ行っておしゃべりをする。彼女が準備している畑は、ぼくの小さなジャガイモ畑の二〇倍もの大きさだ。

この家族用の野菜畑は二、三年間放置されていて、雑草が一面に生い茂っている。彼女の春の大仕事は、それを復活させることである。彼女は、一枚刃の鋤で土を掘り返した。そして八十四歳の手で、草と根っこを引き抜いた。「夏野菜を植えようと思ってるんだよ」と、彼女はそんな仕事は何でもないという風に言う。

（原文：エドワード・レヴィンソン　訳：鶴田静）

Edward Levinson (Japan/ Chiba/ USA)

From *Whisper of the Land (5)*（『ぼくの植え方』英語版）

One spring day I was driving to a nearby valley to photograph the wild wisteria that grows in the mountains. The road was narrow so I parked the truck in a puff-off area and walked, looking for a shot. Oddly, I could hear a radio playing behind some tall grass. An oba-san was working in a vegetable patch and her radio keeping her company. I waved and she waved back, so I braved a tall grass and possibility of snakes to go over and chat with her.

She was working in a field twenty times the size of my tiny potato patch. A family vegetable garden, it had been neglected for a couple of years and the weeds had taken over. Her spring project was to resurrect it. With just a spade she had turned over the soil, and with her eighty-four –years-old hands pulled out weeds and roots.

Old farmer woman with traditional headscarf
姉さんかぶりの農婦

『燃える風船』より（俳句と写真）

雲踊る
蛙歌う
月告げる
地が揺れる
静止する
神秘のとき

Harmony: Frog and Iris
調和：カエルとアイリス

From Balloon on Fire (haiku & photo)

Clouds dance
Frogs sing
Moon warns
Earth quakes
Stillness comes
Special moment

kumo odoru, kaeru utau, tsuki tsugeru,
chi ga yureru, seishi suru, shinpi no toki

コロナ渦
CORONA TIMES

corona times
broken plans
life goes on

コロナ渦や予定壊れる生き直す
Korona ka ya yotei kowareru iki naosu

An old abandoned schoolhouse in Kamogawa, Chiba Prefecture.
(This haiku came to me as I was taking the photo.)
廃校の学校、千葉県鴨川市。
(撮影しながらこの句が生まれました。)

<会員近況報告・メール情報他> *PANDORA NEWS*

パンドラ・ニュース１

PANDORA NEWS (1)

手を結ぶ世界の詩人たち
新型コロナウイルス感染症の中で
「東京ポエトリー・リーディング2020、ズーム大会」

水崎野里子

多元言語使用可の「東京ポエトリー・リーディング」開催はもう５回目くらいになるが、オンラインを駆使したズーム大会は本年初めてである。

本年前半、コロナ感染拡大で日本詩人クラブの例会も含み、諸会合やオペラや芝居など、いわゆる「三密」のイベントはほとんどすべてキャンセル、中止あるいは順延となっていた。東京オリンピックは既に順延決定。東京のコロナ感染グラフは日に日に高まって行った。結果として、地方の大学がそろって、教職員、家族が県境を越えて東京に入ることを禁じてしまった。ある大学は入った者は帰って２週間の自宅待機を決めた。

メールやテレビニュースなどで、日本の大学では本年前半の授業はほとんどオンラインを使用していると知り、詩人会でその応用を思いついた。そこでまず、東北の大学に勤務しているスコット・ワトスン先生（米国ペンシルベニア州出身、現在仙台在住。詩人・俳人・翻訳家、東北学院大学教授）にホスト（ズーム操作係）をお願いしたら、ＯＫをいただいた。ただ、大学の個人アドレスを使用するので、学生を入れた授業の一環で、という条件が付いた。ＯＫ。同じく会員のエドワード・レビンソンさん（米国バージニア州出身、現在千葉県鴨川に在住。

詩人、写真家、エッセイスト、園芸家）は日本とアメリカの大学などを往復する国際人であるので、ズーム操作についてよくご存じのようであった。

「ポエトリー・リーディング・イン 東京、ズーム大会 2020」の詳細は以下に報告する。

8月13日、午前10時から正午まで。大会の参加者と朗読詩は以下である。藤田晴央（日本・弘前）、英語版「Mt.Iwaki」（「岩木山」、英訳水崎野里子）、ドイツ語版 「Schneeflocken」（「雪」、ドイツ語訳ご自作）。スコット・ワトスン（アメリカ・仙台）、英語俳文「Kenji Country」。プリーティ・セングプタ（インド・ニューヨーク）、「Taiyo no Haiku」抜粋。志田道子（日本・東京）、英語「I feel fine though」。Igawa Michiko, Shiraishi Misuzu（日本、お二人ワトスン先生の英語俳句のお弟子さん）。Shiraishi Misuzu（俳名・深心川）、英語俳句「Lake Tanuma」。水崎野里子（日本・東京）、英語版「Haiku On Corona」と司会進行補助。エドワード・レビンソン（アメリカ・千葉鴨川）、カエルの写真（ズームでは写真も映像で流せる）、六行俳句を英語と日本語で朗読。詩集『燃える風船／ Balloon on Fire』序文エッセイ「Touch of Light 光と触れ合う」を日本語と英語にて。最後にウベ・ワルター（ドイツ・京都）、氏は京都北山山頂ヒュッテ在住、詩人、エッセイスト、尺八名手、大蔵流パーフォーマーというマルチタレントで京都ばかりではなく東京を含む日本各地、アメリカ、ドイツなど海外でもパーフォーマンス経験多いアーチストである。多忙の中、私の参加要請メールをご覧になり前日夜に電話下さり、「音楽が最後に入った方が楽しくていいんじゃない？」と滑り込みセーフのご参加となった。北山の自宅の山荘より参加で、山荘から見る広大な京都北山風景をズームに映した。「どこですか？　ヒマラヤ？　あれ？　日本の風景だ！」と日本家屋の屋根建築を見ておっしゃるワトスン先生との質疑応答のあと、スピーチと尺八演奏、相馬民謡。英語使用。ズーム大会は正午過ぎに終了。お疲れ様でした。

ワトスン先生はうまくズーム詩人会をホスト操作、進行なさった。

時々、参加者の情報を知っている私がズームで相手と対話した。プリーティさんとはほぼ8年ぶりの再会であった。しばし再会の対話。長い年月とニューヨークとトウキョウの長い距離とインドとアメリカと日本という3つのボーダー（国境）を軽々と超えて再会できたズーム大会であった。メカニック、ITの発展には御礼申し上げたい。

（「詩と思想」2020年12月号より）

On Tokyo Poetry Reading in Zoom, 2020

Dear My Friend Poets:
Hi! How are you going? In the world wide corona spreading and, together with usual natural disasters, like flooding.
By the way, please join us, The Tokyo Poetry Reading in Zoom, 2020 (Or PANDORA Readings).
The Information below:
The Date & Time: August 13th, Start at 10:00 a.m. Please count the time difference between you and Tokyo time. Japan local time is thirteen hours ahead of Florida, or New York. In California, more.
The Host: Professor Scott Watson, from US, now living in Sendai, Japan. Professor of Tohoku Gakuin University. He is a Translator of Basho, and Santoka. He can read his poems, too.
Languages: English and Japanese. English the first and, Japanese the second.

If you can join us, please mail to Professor Scott Watson: He will give you, what to do with Zoom meeting.

We are looking forward to seeing you, in zoom, together.
Best Wishes,
Noriko Mizusaki
Pandora editor
From Tokyo

ズーム大会おしらせの英文手紙

2020年（令和2年）8月26日　（水曜日）

陸奥新報

文化

寄稿

オンラインによる詩の朗読会

遠くの人と呼び交わす大切さ

藤田晴央

今年は新型コロナウィルスのために様々な催しが中止になっているが、9月に東京で予定されていた詩の朗読会も中止となった。しかし、そのままではいけないと、先ごろ、オンラインにより詩人・俳人たちが顔を合わせた。もともと、日本語の詩を外国語で紹介している「パンドラ」が主催の催しで「ポエトリー・リーディング・イン東京、ズーム会2020」と銘打たれた。「ズーム」とは遠方にいる人たちが画面分割の形で一堂に会することが出来るインターネットのアプリケーションである。

当日は、仙台市在住のスコット・ワトスンさんがホストとなり、主催者で船橋市在住の詩人・水崎野里子さんなどアメリカや日本各地から11人が参加し、2時間に渡って熱のこもった朗読会が開かれた。

現在の社会状況を反映してコロナウィルスに触れた作品もいくつかあった。中でも東京から参加した志田道子さんの英語詩「I feel fine though」は「誰が地球終焉の危険を冒しているのか／野心が多すぎ、張り合いが多すぎ、馬鹿騒ぎが多すぎる／今、自然は私たちに彼自身の薬・コロナを与えているのかもしれない」（日本語訳・藤田）と、人類の在り方に警鐘を鳴らす詩句が盛り込まれており、強いインパクトを持つものだった。

私は、弘前市立郷土文学館で開催中の「岩木山と文学」に出品中の詩「岩木山」を英語（水崎／藤田共訳）で、「雪」をドイツ語（モニカ・ウンケル／藤田共訳）で朗読した。インド出身でニューヨーク在住のプリーティ・セングプタさんは「ナマステと私は言う／（略）／分かち合うのに充分な愛がある／ニューヨークと東京の間に／私とあなたの間に」（日本語訳・藤田）とbetween（間）を結ぶ愛を描いた詩を朗読。ワトスンさんは、山頭火や宮沢賢治の詩を英語俳文にして紹介、映像作家でもあるエドワード・レビンソンさん（鴨川市）は「Touch of Light」（光と触れ合う）などを朗読、最後に京都在住のドイツ人ウベ・ワルターさんが、福島県相馬地方の民謡を尺八で披露し、その流麗な奥深い響きが各地を結んだ。

オンラインによる詩の朗読会で自作詩「岩木山」の英語訳を披露する筆者。参加者は画面で詩を活字で見ることができる。画面右には参加者が映っている

私自身は、コロナウィルスによって、対面のコミュニケーションが失われ、それがオンラインによって代替されていく状況を良いとは思っていない。表現行為はもちろん、大学の講義なども対面によって得られるものは大きい。しかし、ウィルス感染が収束しない中、ある種の排他的な雰囲気も生まれている状況にあって、インターネットを通じて「遠くにいる人」「異なる人たち」と呼び交わすことはとても大切なことだと思う。このような閉塞的な社会状況が一日でも早く終わることを祈りつつ、居住している国や県をこえた詩人たちの催しについて報告させていただく。

（詩人、東北女子大学非常勤講師）

※「ポエトリー・リーディング・イン東京、ズーム会2020」は13日に行われた

藤田様ご報告発表

パンドラ・ニュース2

PANDORA NEWS (2)

THE LIGHT OF THAT SUMMER

対訳　朝倉原爆被害者の会証言集

A Collection of Testimonies by Members of the Asakura Atomic Bomb Victims' Association

Translated from *Inochi Kanashiki* (2012)

Supplemented with Testimonies by Survivors of the March 11, 2011 Earthquake, Tsunami and Nuclear Power Plant Disaster

編著者　徳永節夫
コーディネーター　石川晶子

徳永節夫氏の上掲の著書が、中村朋子さんの、日本で英語で書かれたヒロシマ原爆資料・記録を集めたアーカイヴ、＜リンガヒロシマ＞に掲載された。サーチは「徳永節夫Search Results Lingua Database.html」
ちなみに、徳永節夫は詩人草倉哲夫さんの本名。

編著者：徳永節夫『対訳　朝倉原爆被害者の会証言集　補填　2011年3月11日の地震・津波・原発破壊の生存者の証言』（2011年8月1日発行、朝倉原水爆禁止協議会発行、「朝倉原爆被害者の会」協力）覚書
解説：水崎野里子

本著作は2011年8月1日に発行された。福岡県朝倉市に住む徳永節夫さんから水崎野里子に寄贈いただいた本である。2011年8月1日というと、大被害を及ぼしたあの東日本大震災から五か月後であり、実に素早い徳永氏の統率と刊行作業であり、氏の時代を見極める洞察の明晰さと鋭さには驚嘆の思いである。

私事で恐縮であるが、デヴィッド・クリーガー作、水崎野里子翻訳の詩集『神の涙――広島・長崎原爆.／国境を越えて 』の初版は2010年8月6日である。当時は、世界的には反核の運動が盛り上がっていた時期であり、日本国内においては声が高まり始めた時期にあたる。その波にうまく乗ってくれた証言集という御礼と、ヒロシマ・ナガサキにやがてフクシマが加わる三者一体を一早く具現させた証言集である。感嘆と称賛とがある。称賛はまだある。朝倉という福岡県の一地域、長崎県に隣接する福岡県内に位置するが、ヒロシマ・ナガサキ・フクシマの名ほどにはまるで一般には知られていない、マイノリティの地域性を取り上げた。一般に、世界的にも日本国内においてもほとんど知られていないゆえにより大きく響く、無名の市民・犠牲者の証言者たちの声を集めた貴重な証言集と評価する。

収められた証言のほとんどが70歳代から80歳代（出版当時）の一般市民であり、2011年8月刊行は、彼ら、彼女たちの証言を集め得るギリギリの時期でもあっただろうと、私は証言作者の年齢を次々と確認しながら思っていた。80歳代が多い。素早くギリギリの時間で決行した、徳永さんの決断と実行力と組織力は感嘆の他はない。

気づいたことはまだある。皮膚の爛れと剥れ、水を求める被害者たち、紫斑、内出血、白血病、遺伝、建築物の破壊と犠牲者、とくに近親

者による死去した近親者の火葬などは広島関係の証言で聞くのと同じ症状と状況であること、(広島のウラニウム爆弾と長崎のプルトニウム爆弾の症状はことなるという叙述を読んだことがある)、次いで、朝倉の人々が学徒動員や兵役などでかなり長崎・佐世保、広島・呉などに出向いていて被爆していることである。結果として、長崎・広島に投下されたはずの原爆がかなり離れた朝倉の住民にも多大な被害を及ぼした。言い換えれば、被爆者への差別や反核運動の屈折などの理由で、彼らが証言できるのは70歳代、80歳代まで待たなければならなかったのか、そしてフクシマ原発の津波破壊と危険地域からの人々の立ち退き損害(自殺したおばあちゃんもいた)との対比を待たなければならなかったのかというもどかしさの認識は残る。その点もあり、フクシマ原発地域の当時の日本政府による強制移動居住の現実の補足対比は明察だ。彼らも差別を受けた。だが一方では、立ち退かないで危険地域に住んでいたりとどまっていては、被爆の危険はますます大きかったはずだ。当時、米国などによる当時の〈被爆危険地域〉の設定は、日本政府の出すデータよりもかなりの広範地域に及んでいた記憶がある。大地震と津波を予期できなかったフクシマ原発破壊の悲惨を人災と取るか天災と取るかは現在でもなお微妙な問題であるが、立ち退きを余儀なくされた被害者の悲しみと苦労と他県での差別は、今後なお忘れ得ない問題として残るだろう。喉元を過ぎれば我々すぐに忘れ去る。一方では、過去にいつまでもこだわっていても始まらない。だがまた、核兵器拡散条約がほとんど反古同然である今、現在という新たな時代の中で、本書をもう一度改めて読み返すことは無駄ではないだろう。エネルギー問題は常に犠牲と戦争を含む葛藤と大国の利権と圧制を露呈して来た。

最後になるが、海外での一時の英語発表の原爆詩の盛り上がり(2004～2014頃)を日本に移植する経緯で私が気づいたことがある。そのひとつは、日本人は細かな、うるさいセクトに分かれ、容易に団結しない(できない)ことであり、長崎と広島両市の連帯さえもかなりむずかしいという発見と事実であった。広島関係のイベント開催を長崎関係の有力者に依頼しても梨のつぶてであり、その逆もまた真であった。徳永さんは故郷朝倉を愛する詩人(詩人としてのペンネームは草倉哲夫)であるが、その朝倉グループを簡単にまとめ、統率してしまった。おまけに正確で明快な英訳までつけ、カナダの大学のプロフェッサーの協力まで簡単に短期間で取り付けてしまった。見事である。これは驚きとしてある。

日本の今後の平和活動に必要なものは、この一致団結と素早さであり、セクトを超えて、あるいはセクトの多様性を保ちつつ明確な現状分析を伴いながら世界平和の下に一致団結し得る力である。それを国際性と言い換えてもいいだろう。本証言集の刊行に、遅まきながら徳永節夫さんに心より御礼を申し上げたい。

なお、本書は広島の呉に在住の中村朋子教授により、日本において英語で発表された原爆資料を集めたアーカイヴ、〈リンガヒロシマ〉に入れていただいた。中村朋子さんにも心より御礼申し上げる。女史は一貫して反核兵器の平和活動を持続している。女史の持続する意思、これも見事である。

パンドラ・ニュース3

PANDORA NEWS (3)

働淳さんより送・三池の地域文化保護と発展

パンドラ・ニュース4

PANDORA NEWS (4)

2020年水崎野里子海外交流

2020年6月：日本・マルタ島アート交流展作品参加（クリエイト・アイエムエス企画）。

2020年9月：BESETO三都市市長会議ソウル展（「ソネット・ミラベル宮殿の赤い薔薇」で作品参加。美術の杜出版社関与）。

2020年7月より参加開始：カリフォルニアPOVズーム詩人会参加：1か月2回、第2週と第4週の金曜日、6：30pm開始（日本時間翌日土曜日10：30am）。約1時間半。毎回参加者6～7人。英語使用。日本からは参加者水崎野里子1名。カリフォルニア詩人による英語ハイク発表もあり。

安森ソノ子海外交流と活動

2020年11月：フランスのジャポニズム・スフセサール芸術勲章を受勲。モネ誕生180周年記念事業にて。

2021年1月18日：同志社大学「新島襄研究会」1月例会にて（今出川キャンパス至誠館S2番教室）「新島襄の遺墨より」発表。本研究会はZoomによるオンライン研究会。水崎野里子ズームにより聴講。

会員間のメール交換１

植木信子さんと水崎野里子

植木信子様
おたよりありがとうございました。お元気なご様子で嬉しく存じます。この3か月、イベントは全部キャンセルで自宅自閉の毎日です。怖いですね。自然がニンゲンに復讐しているような気がしています。あるいはどこかが仕掛けた黴菌戦争か？と、初めは思いました。いいお薬とワクチンが出来ることを祈るばかりです。でもそうなったら、また新型が現れるかもね。お互い注意して生きましょう。水崎拝
＊パンドラ刊行が大幅に遅れています。このような事態ですので少しもっと待ってもいいと思います。いい時期に刊行・配布したいですよね。

のり子様
コロナは首都圏は大変のようでしたね。新潟県は、でもゴールデン・ウィークなどやお花見の頃はいろいろと大変でした。時間があると内面的になりますね。それはそれで貴重かもなどどおもったりしていました。ただこのコロナは人間が人間あらしめる行為を封じ込めるのです。何かのたたりのような、それとも人間の傲慢さを思いしらしめているような。
＊呪いだと、昔の人だったら言うでしょう。私もはじめはそう思いました。
信子

植木信子様
お知らせありがとうございました。ご無事でなによりでございます。コロナ騒ぎはだいぶ大変ですね。昨日テレビで亭主が「荒神」というドラマを見ていましたがそういうことなのかとも思います。新型ウイ

ルスはあちこちで妙な症状と結びつき変形して人間を襲うアラガミなんでしょう。アラガミと戦っているわけですがお医者様とか医療関係の方々の犠牲はご冥福をお祈りするしかないです。
ただカーテンを洗ったり年末にさぼった大掃除をしたりする時間はあります。でないと運動不足。
人間の「出会い」、「集まり」をシャットしているのですからもう世も末です。アラガミ退治に励みましょう。でもお医者様に励んでもらえるように庶民はお祈りするしかないです。ではまた。パンドラも少し遅れています。じっと我慢の子でお待ちください。水崎野里子拝

水崎様
コロナは本当に戦争下ではこんなだったのかもと思わせますね。でも収束しなければ大切な生きられた命が消えてしまうのですから、微生物も人と戦っているのかも。メール嬉しいでした。来年の今ころは毎日が日曜日に近くなるのであちこちにメールを送るのではないかと心配しています。パンドラ楽しみにしています。またお会いできますように。コロナに感染しませんようお元気でいらしてください。
信子

会員間のメール交換2

ウベ・ワルターさんと水崎野里子

Dear Noriko,
This, I wrote in German and translated it into English. And added a poor japanese translation.

コロナが転んだ

The sun bent over the edge of the universe: Incredibly she mumbled.
“At night the earth is shining like the full moon? There, right back there, there is still a bit of darkness.”
She says and bends even lower and lower and she dropped her corona. The sun crown shattered right on the Nanga Parbat Mountain. A strong wind arose and carried the stardust to every nook and corner of the earth.
It was inhaled and exhaled again - while singing, speaking, laughing. Whoever breathed it in stopped moving. Everything stopped moving:
The rusted gears of the shovel excavators, mine shafts and oil drill pipes in the thawing Antarctica, even the conveyor belts around the blast furnaces came to a standstill. No Tomato juice from Turkey. Silence.
Except for the calming sound of the breakers, the murmur of a river. And a warm summerbreeze carries the joyful churping of the birds.
Dazed, the people staggered out of their cramped houses, rubbed their eyes as if awakened after a long sleep.
The parks were full of people lying on their backs and gazing at the clouds in ecstasy.
Some painted posters with “A new time begins!” Or: “Thanks to our earth.”
Hostile states promised to disarm, the Amazon was reforested, Las Vegas turned its gambling houses into adventure parks and the investment banks organized barbequs rosting their steaks on bad loans.Thanks to the gods, we

have been getting off pretty lightly. This time.

太陽は宇宙の端から地球の裏側を見て。「信じられない」彼女はつぶやいた。夜中でも、地球は満月のように輝いている。
「あ、そこに、すぐそこに、まだ少し暗闇が残っている」と言いながら、さらに身を乗り出しながらコロナが転んだ。ナンガパルバット山脈に激突した。上がってきた強風に運ばれた、スターダストを吸い込んだ人の動きを止めました。すべての動きが止まった。
解凍かけている南極の石油ドリルパイプや鉱山シャフト、ショベル掘削機の錆びたギア、高炉の周りのコンベヤーベルトさえも停止た。沈黙。
夏の落ち着いた潮の音、川のせせらぎ、そよ風が鳥のうれしそうな鳴き声を運んだ。
ぼんやりと、街の人々は窮屈な家からよろめき、長い眠りの後に目覚めたかのように目をこすった。
公園に仰向けになって雲を見つめる人々でいっぱいだった。「新しい時代が始まる！」または「地球に感謝」と書いたポスターが壁に貼ってある。
敵対国は武装解除を約束し、アマゾンは再植林され、ラスベガスはギャンブルハウスをアドベンチャーパークに変え、投資銀行は麗らかな夏の日の焼肉パーティー燃えている不良債権の上で炒めた。神々のおかげで、私達はかろうじて逃れた。今回は。

Dear Uwe Walter san:
Hi! This morning I called you two times, but no answer. Are you safe? or staying abroad? In Germany?
At any rate, if you are so busy sending poems to our magazine, can not I copy your mails on Pandora to me, with mine, as mailing exchanges?
I am afraid I am having no time to put them into Japanese, but your questioning on Pandora is interesting. Japanese people read Greek myths

only on the knowledge: while you worship them as your real faiths. A cultural gap, though Shakespeare used the Pandora caskets legend in his play, in *The Merchant of Venice*. If you do not like the copy, tensai, 転 載, mail back to me.

If you all right, you do not have to mail back. I know you are busy. Till 20th of November.

With my Best Regards, Noriko

Guten Morgen

あとがき

本年も皆様に『パンドラⅥ』をお送りします。海外詩人と日本詩人協力のアート誌、日本語と他言語（英語メイン）使用の、日本では数少ないマルチリンガル誌として果たすべき役割は大きく、本年も境を越えた世界の友好と平和を世界へ向けて発信します。会員・投稿の皆さまの結束と協力とご寛容は本年も大きく、感謝・御礼申し上げます。

昨年2020年11月から世界的に拡がったコロナ感染被害の中で、みなさまのご苦労も大きかったし、いまだ収束しておりません。皆さまのご自愛をくれぐれもよろしくお願い申し上げます。ご健勝をお祈りします。

末筆になりますが本号もブックウエイ出版社と編集の黒田貴子様にお世話いただきました。
こころより御礼申し上げます。

2021年春吉日
パンドラ刊行委員会
水崎野里子

「パンドラⅥ」

刊 行 日：2021年3月28日
版権取得：2021年3月28日
発 行 所：273-0031千葉県船橋市西船2-20-7-204水崎方
「パンドラ」刊行委員会
Eメールアドレス：the-mizusaki@pop21.odn.ne.jp
ファクス・電話：047-434-8579
印刷所・発売元：学術研究出版（姫路）
TEL：079-222-5372　FAX：079-244-1482
Eメール：bookway@arpub.jp
https://arpub.jp

ISBN978-4-910415-40-6
「パンドラⅥ」はE-Bookとしても購入可能です。
紙製本・電子本：1,700円（+税）US$17.00

The First Edition: March 2021.
Copyright: March 2021
The Members' Office of the PANDORA Books:
c/o Noriko Mizusaki,
2-20-7-204, Nishifuna, Funabashi-shi, Chiba, 273-0031, Japan
TEL/FAX: 047-434-8579, International: 81-47-434-8579
The Publication & Sales Store: Academic Research Publication (in Himeji, Japan)
TEL 079-222-5372 FAX: 079-244-1482
E-mail: bookway@arpub.jp
https://arpub.jp
ISBN978-4-910415-40-6

You can also read "PANDORA VI" in the E-Book.
A Paper Book & E-Book: ¥1,700 (+tax)　US$17.00
刊行日時：2021年3月28日